LAMLASH STREET

Red Damask
PUBLISHING

PUBLISHING

Red Damask Publishing
http://www.jmphillipsauthor.com

ISBN: 9781777258504 (print)
ISBN: 978-1-7772585-2-8(ebook)

Ordering Information:
Special discounts are available on quantity purchases by corporations, associations, and others. For details, contact jmphillipsauthor@outlook.com

LAMLASH STREET

A 1963 PORTRAIT OF POST-WAR LONDON THROUGH ONE FAMILY'S STORY

J. M. PHILLIPS

Red Damask
PUBLISHING

DEDICATION

To all the powerful Walters women,
who kept their families together through thick and thin,
and thin and thin…

INTRODUCTION

This is the story of life in one small street in London in 1963. Certainly, it was a time when the Beatles, Twiggy, and Carnaby Street were always in the papers, but behind the 'swinging sixties' there lurked a sadder time, when you consider that just 18 years earlier the country had been at war and people like my uncle, at the age of just 17, had witnessed his friends dying. So although the sixties may appear to us now to be about fun, the age of free expression, and no responsibility, the reality is that we were all dealing with the recent aftermath of war.

While there was fun to be had, there was also sadness and anxiety. This story is about what it was really like to live in this time of great change; to be raised by people still recovering from the shell-shock and stress of the Blitz, and the near starvation of WWII; to grow up in a decade so close to major world events and yet to live in a close-knit community, in working-class London, in the microcosm of Lamlash Street. And so here we are in the Christmas of 1962, which heralded in 1963, a year of tremendous change and social turmoil.

CONTENTS

CHAPTER 1

CHRISTMAS 1962

In London, Christmas 1962, one small street and the people who lived there faced a future of extinction. We would face more challenges in the year to come than we had in the whole duration of the recent war. This was a time of much transition for my family and me; my life changed in ways that I could not imagine and really did not want to happen. Up until now my life had been perfect and then 1963 happened: what should have been a time of carefree fun, became a time of stress and self-preservation.

I grew up at 11b Lamlash Street, in an area of London known as the Elephant and Castle, always shortened to 'the Elephant'. The name dates back to at least Shakespeare's time and maybe even Henry VIII's reign. Back then, the Beatles were on the front page of the newspapers every day and my mum and dad would complain that there was no 'real news' because all the papers could write about was these long-haired singers.

Lamlash is an unusual name. It was apparently named after a village on the Isle of Arran, an island north of Scotland, and the training location for the Scottish Commandos of WWII. The street itself was very narrow, with only a single lane, the width of one car. Cars very rarely came down the street anyway, as most people used buses or the Tube to get about, and a lot of Londoners couldn't afford a car. My gang of friends and I would use the entire neighbourhood and its battered war-torn nooks and crannies as our playground—the only one we really had.

My name is Jill and this is my story, from knowing it all to feeling that I knew absolutely nothing about how life really worked. I suppose I was a slightly unusual 10-year-old and didn't quite meet the expectations of the times I lived in. I didn't fit the 'girly-girl' mould; in fact, to be honest, I wanted to change the mould as it was so restrictive and did not suit me at all well. But more of that later.

I was raised in the 1960s by a caring family, who were still recovering from the shock and horror of the Blitz and the severe food shortages of WWII. We lived in a small community, in a poor working-class cockney area of London.

Now a cockney Londoner is someone born within the sounds of the church bells of St Mary-le-Bow in Cheapside, London. And as I was born in a hospital just across from Waterloo train station—albeit under dire circumstances, according to Mum—then I certainly qualified for this honour.

In day-to-day life, my family spoke in cockney rhyming slang, so it was normal for us to say, 'trouble and strife' in place of 'wife', the husbands would often say, 'here comes me trouble'. Or we would use the words 'plates of meat' instead of feet. A really common phrase to hear after a trip to East Lane Market was 'me dogs are barking', which means my feet are aching, as the words 'dog meat' rhyme with 'feet'. Certain phrases were shortened every time they were used, and so Mum would often say, 'Jill, why don't you go up the apples and comb your Barnet.' This meant that I should go upstairs (apples and pears) and comb my hair (Barnet Fair). As well as using rhyming slang, cockneys also dropped the letter 'h' so that 'house' became 'ouse'; and the letters 'th' became 'v', so instead of 'with' we would say 'wiv'.

There is a myth that the cockney dialect was invented as a way of hiding criminal acts from the police. I am not sure if this is true, but one effect this language definitely had was that it drew our small community together. We would proudly use our cockney slang as a way of showing who we were. We identified strongly with this strange 'other' language; it set us apart from the rest of the world. It was a wonder really that I had any command of traditional English at all, and I secretly thought of myself as bilingual, speaking both cockney and real English as the need arose.

Against this cockney backdrop, Mum's approach was a little different from most other members of our family. She always wanted the best for us, so from an early age there were clues in the way she brought us up that we were expected to be better than average, which very much reflected Mum's own personality. She was a highly intelligent woman and emphasised to us the importance of education, which in 1960s working-class London was unheard of.

Children at that time were told by their parents to leave school as soon as it was legal—at age 15—so that they could start to contribute financially to the family upkeep. To encourage me to do well in school, Mum would say to me, 'You can either be the man sweeping the streets, or if you study well, you can be the man *supervising* the man who sweeps the streets and get paid more.' In those days, the word 'man' also included women, although we were rarely mentioned in leadership roles. The choice was obvious to me: Study hard and then spend your life telling other people what to do. This seemed to me to be a good deal.

But back to Lamlash Street, which was originally built in the late 1800s as part of the Faraday Estates. Michael Faraday was a Victorian philanthropist committed to improving living conditions of the working classes in Dickensian London. His ideals and those of Charles Dickens and people, such as Angela Burdett-Coutts, was to improve the lot of the poor and uneducated by giving them good housing, educating children, and giving families hope for a productive future and a healthy life.

These benevolent Victorians could not, however, have foreseen the impact that two world wars would have on the poor working classes. In London, we now tend to think of trauma from wars as being something that happens 'somewhere else'. Yet when I was born, there was still food rationing. *All Our Yesterdays*, a popular TV show at the time, talked constantly about life during WWII, when England was under siege—how families would be stretched to feed the household and how growing vegetables was essential to keep enough food on the table.

However, beyond the day-to-day austerity, there was also a hidden impact of living through the war and the Blitz, one that has shaped the lives of my family for three generations. How could the war not have touched the people who raised me when one sunny day, as young schoolgirls, my mum and aunt were strafed by machine-gun fire from a WWII fighter plane on the way home from school and had to dive into the bushes to escape. Or when my uncle was given the 'White Feather' of cowardice in a pub at the age of 17 but was also at the Battle of the Atlantic. And how could it not affect his very soul when my father at the age of 11 would watch the explosions and destruction of the Blitz of London, night after night from the rooftops, listening out for flying bombs, when his 'toy' collection was pieces of shrapnel to take home (if indeed his home was still there the next day). The adults smoked and drank as a way of coping with the daily trauma of being bombed and not knowing if their friends and family would still be alive the next morning.

But to me, during the Christmas of 1962, the adults' talk was all doom and gloom. You have to remember that 1962 had been a year of much excitement but also uncertainty. It was the year in which John Glenn became the first American to orbit the Earth, when Marilyn Monroe was found dead in the nude in questionable circumstances, when Britain was testing underground nuclear weapons in Nevada. And in October of that year, it had been the year that the world had come to the brink of war again, during the Cuban Missile Crisis, when Russia tried to place nuclear missiles within striking distance of the United States. It was a time of almost weekly Ban the Bomb peace marches to Aldermaston, the military base where the UK's nuclear weapons were located. It felt as if any day there would be a nuclear warhead flying over London, just as the Doodlebugs (flying bombs) had flown over my parents during the Blitz just 20 years earlier.

In 1962, London was known as the trendiest place on the planet. Every day we would read about The Beatles' music and their latest exploits. Jean Shrimpton and her slim figure (in stark contrast to the curves of the models in the 1950s) would grace the front page of *Vogue* magazine. Carnaby Street was the only place to shop for outer-space-inspired clothes, such as your A-line dress in shiny white plastic material. Or to find that all-new trend of bell-bottom trousers.

So, the sixties may conjure an image of swinging London, men wearing long hair and 'young people's' music. But we were still very much living with the aftermath of WWII.

Lamlash was one of the streets which somehow survived the war, but other streets were not as lucky. Just a few hundred yards away whole buildings had been razed to the ground. After the war, there was a serious housing shortage because of the many homes destroyed by enemy bombs; whole blocks of land were now nothing more than empty bomb sites.

Sadly, within a year most of the people and the culture of my street would be transformed and me along with it. But for now, this was the Christmas of 1962 and I had my mind on happier things. We had just had our big Christmas party to which all our family and friends had come to celebrate the season.

Despite all of this gloom, Mum always made sure that we had a great Christmas, which was always topped off with a large party of over a hundred people. As usual, preparations for Christmas had started back in November, with the order-ing of party supplies and as the big day drew closer, the huge Victorian living room of 11b had been hung with decorations as close as we could get to the high ceilings. In those days, very few people drank wine or cocktails—it was whiskey, gin, beer, and lemonade. The beer was a dark brown ale—no lager or light beer. Kids would be given lemonade, with the occasional taste of alcohol from a friendly relative by way of a sip of beer.

The Christmas party had been held in the living room, with the furniture pushed against the walls for people to sit on, this also made room for a large dancing area in the middle of the floor. Uncle and Dad had been tasked with moving every chair in the house to the living room in readiness for the party guests. In addition to the dining room chairs being moved they also used the living room three-piece suite. This consisted of a settee and two armchairs, which was made of the new cutting-edge vinyl in grey and red with black buttons. The living room wallpaper was a coordinating red flock and the carpet was, of course, red as well. Mum always believed in having a modern, organised, and coordinated environment to live in, and she was the only one in her large family to think in this way. Whenever we visited the homes of uncles and aunts, they always seemed so old-fashioned, with over-used armchairs that sagged when you sat in them. There was certainly no sagging in our home, neither in the furniture, décor, nor the people who lived there. All thanks to Mum.

Having recently turned 10, I was certain that I knew everything about life. I knew who did what and what I was expected to do. I knew what happened yesterday, what would happen tomorrow and all the days in the near future. A comforting feeling to know so much.

My brother, Paul, was three years younger than me, and to say we were very different would be an understatement. He was the joker of the classroom and I was the serious student. He was always playing outside, would come home with cuts and bruises, and be covered in dirt. I would always be clean and tidy. Being my younger brother, I considered him to be generally a nuisance, but he was important in one highly significant way: We had lots of boys' toys to play with. If Mum had her way, there would have been floor to ceiling girly dolls for me all over the house. Much to Mum's frustration, I had no interest in dolls; I would take the dolly and her pram and 'bury' dolly at the bottom of it where she could not be seen.

Thanks to my brother, I also got to play with his Scalextric electric race car set. I had a train set of my own, too, with a track that was screwed to a large board so all I had to do was attach the wires and add the train and carriages. No other girls had an electric train set, or even cared if they existed, really. I kept these toys to myself.

Christmas to me was always (and still is) one of the most exciting days of the year. I had heard rumours in my class at school that Father Christmas wasn't real, but I was still firm in my resolve that he did exist and that it was he who brought the presents. It made complete sense to me and I argued my point with those who were willing to listen.

On that Christmas, as we waited for our party guests to arrive, my brother and I played with his Scalextric set in his bedroom. Now his blue car was the faster of the two, and so no matter how hard I tried my orange car always came in second, unless he span off the track. The argument that ensued due to the unfairness of the winning odds drew the displeasure of eagle-eared Mum. Just as she was about to pronounce her punishment, we were saved by the bell as the first guests arrived. They were some of my friends from our little gang.

There were five of us, three girls and two boys. Even within our working-class life there were graded strata of achievements. We were all in the top rankings academically and we all came from families who could afford to pay for clean clothes and good shoes for school each day. That put us at or near the top among our classmates, who mostly had very little.

The two boys in our gang were Terry and Anthony; the girls were Barbara and Judy. I always had a secret thing for Terry because his last name and mine were the same, so somehow in my head, I thought we should be a couple. But sadly, he was very firmly focused on Judy, a baby-faced girl who wore a cardigan with small delicate flowers embroidered on it. She had long blonde hair, which she wore in a ponytail that would flip around as she spoke.

So how did this concept of wanting to be in a 'couple' but still being a tomboy fit together? Well it didn't, really; as I said earlier, I didn't fit the mould. This was especially so in the days of strict gender stereotyping and me being just 10 years old. But women's roles were changing; they were actually working in full-time jobs and some even had careers. The expectations of women being only 'housewives' or 'mothers' were beginning to shift and for me that change could not come too soon. So I decided just to keep being my usual self with no dolls but lots of Lego bricks, cars, and trains all in the mix.

As for the size of our extended family, well, it was huge. All of Mum's 12 Walters siblings, who were raised on Penrose Street, had for the most part married the 12 Clark siblings, who were raised on Nicholson Street, which was a 20-minute walk away. So not only was the family large but the relations were complex with everyone knowing everything about both families. Weddings were frequent and there were usually at least 200 people on the 'must invite or we'll never hear the end of it' list. In those days, a different cousin would marry about every six months, and as the family all lived within a five-mile radius of Lamlash Street, various uncles and aunts (with cousins in tow) were always dropping round for cups of tea and endless discussions about the latest family crisis or the next upcoming wedding.

The family, for the most part, did not achieve notoriety, with the exception of Cousin Malcolm, who was found dead in the gutter one morning—something about 'shady dealings' and the local mob. But generally, our family led pretty ordinary lives—raising children, working to put food on the table, and stretching the meagre pennies as far as they would go (through both honest and only occasionally dishonest endeavours).

As usual, Christmas Day had been a multi-event occasion. It had begun with opening our presents at the crack of dawn, followed later by a massive Christmas dinner which, naturally, had finished in time for the Queen's speech at 3 o'clock. There was the usual light tea at 5 o'clock, which had been topped off with the party in the living room, with more food following at 9 o'clock. All of this had as usual been catered by Mum and Auntie, although according to Mum, she did all the sandwich making herself while Auntie did the talking and taking items to and from the kitchen to the living room, of course under Mum's strict supervision.

The party was attended by my immediate family, my uncles, aunts, cousins and some friends who all worked at the Brooks Greeting Card company in the next road that we all called the 'factory'. In those days, you got hired by word of mouth and personal recommendations so the people you worked with were all either family or friends.

The adults had danced, drank, laughed, and exchanged the usual work gossip but with an edge of frustration in their voices. I had noticed that there was a little more seriousness to the conversation, but being only 10, I barely paid it any attention as all of us kids had been busy playing on the stairs. Those Scottish Commandos training near the village of Lamlash on the Isle of Arran, could not have been any more active than we were—sliding down bannisters, jumping down half the flight of stairs at a time, and even 'dangerously' jumping between staircases. I had noticed that Anthony smiled at my antics more than at Judy's or Barbara's but assumed it was just because I was the most adventurous girl there.

As usual, a week later on Old Year's Night, Mum did her customary ritual of opening the back door to let the old year out, then opening the front door to let the new year in. I did always wonder whether this tradition was necessary and it seemed a little ridiculous but it was Mum's rule. It didn't seem quite right, though, that so much heat was lost for this ritual. Ironically, if I had a penny for every time Mum told me to close the doors to keep the heat in, I'd be writing this in a tropical location. I must admit, however, in later years I, too, have let the heat and the years out of my own doors. We wished for a happy year to come as we stood by the front door of our Lamlash home that still to this day I fondly refer to as 11b.

Mum and Dad rented the house, as did everyone on the

street. The concept of owning your own home was not for working-class people like us; that was only for the 'well-to-do'. Although Mum had her own thoughts on this.

Our house was over a hundred years old when we first moved into it and had already been condemned as unfit to live in, however, because of the post-war housing shortage it remained in use as a home. The house had four floors in total with a flat roof on the third and fourth floors. In the upper two floors lived Mum, Dad, me, and my younger brother. Auntie and Uncle lived one flight down on the main floor. Then way down in the dark and damp basement flat lived a 15-year-old girl called Lorraine with her family and their dog, Rex.

The large green front door of 11b was open all day but closed after dark. It had a bronze-coloured Yale lock with a catch on the door for security so even with a key no one could open the door. However, just to be certain to keep any uninvited visitors out, there were also two long black iron bolts, one at the top and one at the bottom of the door, which would be pulled across at night with a solid scraping sound.

The front of 11b was covered in a green creeper (a type of green ivy) that grew all along the top of the brick walls and down one side of the steps and continued down the street and all the way to the houses on the corner. The high walls on the street were great for playing ball games against, of which our favourite was 'Lamlash'. The object was to throw the ball high on the wall to hit the street sign and then jump over the ball after one bounce; it was, for some reason, endlessly fascinating. On the other side of the street was a low wall about six feet high, so it wasn't much good for playing games against but the horizontal iron bars outside the houses were great for using as a trapeze and swinging from them upside down by my legs, my head only clearing the ground by a few inches.

The roof of our house leaked, despite the endless amounts of tar that the landlords repeatedly spread on it. The windows were only single panes with no insulation; the frames were warped and drafty and electric fires would produce only a small amount of heat. Rats would run up the drainpipes outside the house. We had mice in the pantry cupboard and strange small white insects called silverfish that would always be lurking around the wash-hand basin. But to me it was just a nice, normal multi-family house; we each had our own bedroom and there was a spacious living room, a kitchen, and a scullery. We even had an inside toilet—pure luxury.

Our brick-built Victorian house had massive bay windows with 10-foot high ceilings and large, bright and airy rooms. Plaster coving ran along the tops of the walls and ornate ceiling roses surrounded the centre lights. The two big bay, sash-cord windows were always hung with pristine white net curtains. In the mornings, Mum always had the windows open with the curtains blowing in the breeze. She was keen on us having a good 'airing' and to this very day still believes that getting out in the cold weather is the best way of staying free of a cold!

On the same level as the living room was the kitchen, the scullery, and inside toilet. The scullery had hot and cold water and a sink, and this is where vegetables were prepared and the laundry washed by hand. The toilet was one of those high on the wall water closets with a long chain for flushing and sometimes in the winter there was ice in the toilet bowl until, of course, you peed on it. Most people on the street had toilets outside in the garden. They were cold and damp and at night, very scary. In those days, the toilet was not a place to linger in—it was a thing to put off as long as possible.

The main house had two long flights of stairs, which were covered with red padded vinyl, anchored in place with brass rods. Those stairs were great. I can remember jumping from halfway down or sliding down the banisters; we used to love that, me and my brother. The house was filled with places to jump and slide and was just one big playground to us!

Now Mum always had an agenda for our family and she was a great one for getting people to achieve, well, almost anything. Take Dad's particular case. As the sole breadwinner, Mum felt that his income from working at the factory was insufficient for the basic necessities of our family's life so it was agreed that he would become a London black cab driver instead. These are the iconic black taxis that are so much a part of the London landscape and culture. To drive a black cab, you have to pass a very stringent multi-part test of the street routes of London (known as 'appearances'). It's the equivalent of having the entire GPS map of London in your head; this is known as 'The Knowledge'. In those days, it took approximately two years to become a fully-fledged taxi driver. You may ask yourself if it is still necessary to memorise the streets in these days of GPS; the reality is that London roads are so complex that a GPS doesn't always instantly give alternate routes for an obstruction.

Consequently, one day a paper map of London duly appeared on the wall in the living room, and Dad acquired a Moped (which was secondhand and went backwards more than forwards), with a clipboard mounted on the front. The map on the wall was to 'string' the roads for the quickest route between two points by distance. (To this very day, some examiners still use a piece of string to measure the shortest street routes at appearances.) Mum was always in charge of this important job and many hours a day were spent taking a length of cotton from the sewing box and placing it along various roads to determine the shortest route. These routes were then written down in the 'Blue Book', a stenographer's paper pad of routes, of which route No. 1 is Manor House Station to Gibson Square. Dad would then attach this Blue Book to the clipboard of the Moped and spend his days riding up and down streets of London to memorise the routes. On special occasions, I would be permitted to take on the task of call-overs, when Dad would try to orally recall the routes in the Blue Book.

What we did not understand at the time was how his decision to be a cabbie was going to have long-reaching effects on our family's future. But I'll return to that later.

During the time that Dad was riding up and down the streets of London on his Moped, we had to live on a very small income from the government. Dad was paid a disability allowance of £7.2.0 (7 pounds and 2 shillings each week). Now to me, Dad looked perfectly healthy, in fact, when he was feeling extra silly he would actually do cartwheels across the living room floor, much to Mums disgust. So I was curious as to what type of disability he had, but Mum just told me it was none of my business and I never ever heard of Dad having a 'disability' afterwards.

The money he got was really not enough to live on and so he had to borrow money from his own mum, which he paid back when he could. Consequently, after the first year of his training, some austerity measures and some savvy calculations by Mum, the house had a new distraction…not a baby but a cigarette machine! Mum decided to reduce the family cigarette bill by buying cigarettes direct from the cigarette maker, which was cheaper. Up to this point in time, I had been the cigarette runner, as it was considered a child's job to run this errand. I would go to the corner shop to buy the cigarettes, pick up a treat for myself, and take it all home.

So one day, a representative from the cigarette company, Kensitas, came and presented us with a table-top cigarette dispensing machine in a tasteful dark oak colour to match our furniture. It held about 20 packets of cigarettes and when my parents wanted one, they put coins into a little slot and out popped the cigarette packet. The cigarettes also came with vouchers that you collected and could exchange for small appliances and items for the home, the equivalent of a loyalty points scheme today.

The machine made a 'clunk' sound when it dispensed a packet so you could mentally keep track of the remaining inventory, a useful trick that prevented my parents running out of necessary smokes if stress levels rose.... A friend of the family even had a musical cigarette dispenser. It was made of Bakelite, that plastic material. It was fascinating to watch and had eight sides to it with sweet little doors that opened and out popped the cigarettes, all to the sound of a musical tune.

Back in the 1960s there were no health warnings or nic-otine gum; we were not even aware of a connection between cigarette smoking and cancer. People would—gasp—smoke *inside* the house and it was okay; in fact, the concept of standing outside your own house and smoking would have been considered ridiculous. Was everyone being exposed to secondhand smoking? Well yes, but back in the sixties no one had even heard of secondhand or passive smoking. As far as we understood, secondhand smoking would mean smoking with both hands at once! My Aunt Mary even told the tale of a friend whose doctor advised her to smoke as soon as she got up in the morning because it was good for keeping her asthma under control. A very different time!

Every fortnight, the sales rep from Kensitas would come back to collect the money and refill the dispenser. Imagine having an addictive, cancer-causing product in your house today. Well, back in those days it was all perfectly normal.

CHAPTER 2

THE FAMILY

As for my beginnings, I was born at the General Lying-In Hospital, just across from Waterloo Station. Mum tells me that I was a difficult birth and that she was in labour for three whole days, during which time she lay in bed, looking up through the basement window of the delivery room of the hospital, watching the red double-decker London buses go by outside. When I finally emerged into the world with the aid of a pair of forceps, I apparently had terrible red marks and bruises on my face. Of course, Mum could equally well have described it as a wonderfully blissful birth but she did not believe in sugar-coating these significant life events. One of her favourite maxims to live by was to call a spade a spade.

As a 10-year-old girl who loved to ride my bike and was generally a tomboy, I was somewhat questionably matched with a mother who loved to dress me up like a china doll, in frilly dresses and shiny black patent leather shoes with one-inch kitten heels. But I did my best to have one foot in each of these worlds at the same time. I avoided the china-doll persona—and escaped Mum's influence to some extent—by going to school, playing on the streets with my friends, and getting the girly obligations dealt with as early as possible in the day. This freed me up to do the more interesting things in life, such as playing with my Lego set. I would spend all my pocket money on Lego pieces and then spend hours assembling them into houses as scenery for my train set, much to the disappointment of Mum, who couldn't understand why I ignored the china doll in her pram, sitting by itself in the empty hallway, and gathering dust by the front door.

As well as dressing me up, Mum was also a 'clothes horse' herself. She always wore a dress when doing the housework but if it was a really messy job, she would wear ankle-length trousers as part of a fully coordinated ensemble. Mum was actually a stunningly attractive woman but I don't think she ever realised it. She always said, 'clothes maketh the man,' and for that reason, I always seemed to be better dressed than the other kids on the street. For special occasions, I would wear layers and layers of petticoats and airy organza. When not dressed up for a party, I would wear Chanel-style suits or frilly blouses to school. Our school did not have a school uniform, and some of the poorest families had no money for clothes. So when you understand that some children in my class wore the same clothes to school every day, mostly with holes in them, you can see the early conditioning that I was subjected to. To this day, I tend to overdress for the occasion and love to dress for a formal event.

Mum was without a doubt the key organiser at Lamlash, of both our family and Auntie and Uncle. Mum and her sister were raised by a very stern father who was a regimental sergeant major (drill sergeant). Consequently, life was highly organised and for me, very goal-focused. The concept of unconditional love was not one that Mum saw the relevance in. The role of mothers, in her view, was to train children like puppies so that they could succeed in life.

Whereas Mum raised us efficiently, fortunately for me, Auntie did know about unconditional love and so I grew up to be a well-rounded adult with influences from them both. There was always a special bond between Mum and Auntie, due in part from their wartime experiences.

One day, at the beginning of the war, they were coming home from school for lunch and were just outside the library on Walworth Road. Suddenly, they could hear enemy war planes overhead. As the noise got louder, the planes began machine-gunning the streets. People ran about in all directions and Mum and Auntie both dived into the library doorway to escape being hit by bullets.

When they got home, their mother quite simply and calmly said, 'Oh, I can see that you are all right. Just go and eat your lunch.' She then turned back to the other adults and talked matter-of-factly about the school that had been bombed and the children who had died. The sisters ate their lunches in stunned silence and were promptly sent back to school. They passed by the same library on the way back and, looking down, could see the bullet holes in the concrete pavement where they had walked earlier. There was no mental health support back then; they were just two little girls doing what they were told by their mum.

During the Blitz, when German planes flew bombs over London, they and other children were sent to locations throughout England to keep them safe from the nightly devastation. Children were billeted with families who were prepared to take them in for a year. Sadly, not all experiences were positive.

The two sisters, Mum aged 10 and Auntie aged 13, were evacuated together for two years. For the first year, they were sent to a Welsh farmhouse and fed mostly on bread and jam, while the host family ate the extra food rations intended for the sisters. They survived but Mum still remembers how cruel that family was.

The second year, they were evacuated to Somerset, a farming county in Southwest England. The family was kind and they were treated well. However, one day when they were coming home through the fields from school, in school uniform, they heard the unmistakable sound of an aircraft approaching and turned around in horror to see a Nazi Messerschmitt aircraft heading straight for them. It was so close they could see the pilot's face; Mum could describe in detail that he was young and clean-shaven.

The pilot looked directly at them and started firing on

these two schoolgirls; they still remember the ack-ack-ack sound of the bullets hitting the soil just a few feet away. They froze in disbelief before Auntie pulled sharply on Mum's arm and they started running, their school satchels falling in the mud behind them. They ran for the nearest vegetation cover and ended up in a Brussels sprouts patch. Thankfully, the aircraft missed its target and flew over the top of them.

Trembling and white with shock, they ran straight to the family house, only to find that the adults were more concerned about the Woolworths in the village that had been bombed. The only words of solace they received were that there was no real harm done as the bullets had missed. Cold comfort for two little girls far away from home and family, who had almost been killed. Incredibly, for the second time in their short lives, they had been under machine-gun attack by enemy aircraft and had somehow survived. It was no wonder that Mum was always on edge throughout her life and found it difficult to relax, although I suppose the upside was that she or anyone within her sphere of influence did get a lot of things done.

Dad, on the other hand, was a quiet and fairly shy man who, along with his two siblings (one of whom was eventually given away by his mother), was raised by his single parent. His father was a violent drunk, who thankfully disappeared from his life when he was seven years old. They lived on a narrow street just opposite Waterloo Station.

His mother was a young, uneducated woman, who earned a living pushing railway carriages along the track at Waterloo.

When I knew her, she had a curved back, which I was told was the result of being injured by one of the carriages. When she wasn't working, she would escape her life for a more colourful one, just for a while, and enjoy herself at the local pub. Years later, Dad still talked about waiting outside the pub for hours with the other kids, while the adults were inside having a good time. The concept of mental health back then was light years away, and the idea that alcoholism was a sign of stress, that family violence was unacceptable, and that ignoring a child was wrong and could fundamentally damage him was completely foreign to the society of the day.

His mum rented two rooms in the house they lived in. Dad told me years later that their home was sparsely furnished with just the mere basics. They had one double bed in the bedroom, where his Mum slept. Dad's brother would sleep on a camp bed in the alcove of the same room and Dad would sleep on a 'put you up' (sofa) in the living room. The kitchen was shared with all of the other people who rented the house. There were no locks on the doors, so you had to put a chair against the door handle to stop anyone coming into your rooms. He also talked about hearing rats run up and down outside in the guttering of the house. Tough childhood, tough life.

As humorous relief, he would also talk of the times he and his friends would go to the local lunatic asylum, which was known as Bedlam, (its real name was the Bethlem Royal Hospital). They gathered outside the gates laughing at the inmates' bizarre behaviour. This was, apparently, a particularly popular spot for Sunday afternoon entertainment amongst the local working classes. The inmates were usually chained to large lawn mowers, which were dragged across the expanses of grass surrounding the institution. Although this would not be acceptable now, in those days it was considered to be totally acceptable behaviour and a harmless way of passing a Sunday afternoon.

To add to his difficult upbringing, Dad was only 12 at the outbreak of WWII. He was evacuated from London with his mum to escape the bombing, but they returned after six weeks as life in the quiet country was too much of a shock to them after life in London. So Dad spent his formative years living through the Blitz, watching the Doodlebugs (guided flying bombs which were really called V1s) soaring over his neighbourhood; everyone knew that when the flying bomb's engine stopped, they all had to drop to the ground immediately, as the bomb was about to fall from the sky and as it hit the ground it would explode.

Dad, as a young boy, would watch night after night as London was in flames, with explosions and people dying all around him. The bombing took place from 6 o'clock in the evening until the early hours of the next morning to cause maximum chaos for Londoners. Nobody knew if their house would still be standing the next morning or if their neighbours would be alive.

The only adult that provided him with any sense of security was a friendly pastor he called Father Gedge of Southwark Cathedral, where Dad was an altar boy in the church choir. He would attend the choir rehearsals once week and then would don his choir cassock for Sunday service. Thanks to Father Gedge, Dad also attended the church Boy Scouts group, which gave him some sense of belonging.

For some escapism from the nightly terror, Dad would listen to radio broadcasts on the crystal radio set he put together himself. There were no educational toys in those days and the concept of developing a child's mind didn't exist. Families were too busy trying to find money for shoes, clothes and food... and of course, hoping to still be alive the next day.

For Dad, every day was a struggle to survive but at the same time this was his normality. Everyone around him was doing the same thing; struggling to find food and safety when there was little of either to be found.

The working classes had no concept of mental health, and there was certainly almost no treatment for mental illnesses and the conditions in the asylums were appalling. In fact, the need to keep out of the asylum was a way of moderating mild mental illnesses: No one wanted to be committed there. If you were wealthy enough, a sick family member was cared for in the attic or other remote area of the house...well away from prying eyes.

Dad left school as soon as the law permitted, which in those days was at 13. He was quickly put to work at a local cobbler's, making shoes by hand. He still had the cobbler's mould years later and would show it to me and tell me how much he enjoyed it there.

Considering Dad's tough beginnings, it was to his and Mum's credit that they had a steady income over the years and raised two successful children.

The other adult male member of 11b was Uncle. He held the distinction of being one of the very few people who could effectively avoid complying with Mum's many agendas, much to Mum's irritation. He was a tall, jaunty man who always had the time to stop and talk. He was always smiling, saw the good side of people, and enjoyed telling stories of the people he had met. Many years later, just after his passing, I found photographs of Uncle's wartime shipmates. He had kept them for all of those years and they obviously had deep meaning for him.

Uncle always had a slightly embarrassed look about him, due to his reddened face. This was the result of 'blow back' from the boilers of the ship from when he worked as a ship's fireman (stoking the boilers) during WWII. He told me that one day there was a small explosion in the boiler as he shoveled in the coal and he received burns to his face. The engineer with him at the time simply told him to smother engine oil on his face and to go right back to stoking the boiler. That was all the treatment he received for his facial injury. No medical care or psychological counselling, just engine oil and, 'Get back to it, lad.' Beside his obvious injury, Uncle was reluctant to talk about his war stories. I knew that they were sad memories for him. I asked him questions about those days many times but the normally chatty Uncle would not answer me. I was so curious and really wanted to know and so I just kept asking, hoping that he would change his mind one day.

But I did enjoy being with Uncle, as he would talk to me as an adult. He didn't order me about or tell me what I couldn't do. It was just ordinary grown-up talk about issues on the street or discussions about my schoolwork.

Auntie and Uncle lived on the main floor of the house, below us. Auntie was my refuge when I was in the dog house with Mum. She would tell me not to worry and that she would talk to Mum for me. Sure enough, the transgression would soon be forgiven and I could go back to my own world again. Auntie and Uncle did not have any children of their own (something to do with hereditary insanity in the family, as far as I understood) so my brother and I were the children they never had. Mum was highly organised and goal-focused whereas Auntie was laid-back and easy-going. Auntie always seemed happy; she was nonjudgmental and was always pleased to see me. Conversely, Mum always had something for me to do, or achieve or learn. In between the two lies the happy medium, which I achieved by shuffling between the two floors.

However, the impact of the war also changed the dynamics of the family. Uncle John and Uncle Ern had both served as gunners in the RAF, and to have survived in that position until the end of the war was nothing short of a miracle. These two men consequently carried with them a great deal of status and had a huge amount of influence on major family decisions. Additionally, men were always 'in charge' and decided how the money was allocated within the home, and which large purchases, such as furniture were to be made. They were very much the decision-makers, well except, that is, for our corner of the family in which Mum very securely held the reins.

However, even Mum spoke of her brothers, John and Ern, in hushed, reverent tones. Uncle John had been machine gunned in the arm and also still had a piece of shrapnel in his leg that could not be removed and that, according to family legend, was still an open, weeping sore. This made him not just a real war hero but a war hero who was still suffering, which incited a certain deference to any decisions that he made.

CHAPTER 3

THE FACTORY

Just around the corner from Lamlash street was a dark brick Victorian building, which was soon to be highly significant in my life. It had iron bars on the small windows and was originally built as a workhouse for the poor unfortunate souls who had no money and nowhere to live. The workhouse philosophy was that the able-bodied would work for their bed and board. The reality was that they were depressing places and often the inmates, which included children, lived under intolerable and brutal conditions. Nonetheless, workhouses were still in use up until the 1930s, but this building had survived long enough to become the Brooks Print Company, or as it was known to our family, the factory.

During WWII, in order to stay open, the factory carried out government war work, such as printing government pamphlets and posters reminding people that German spies were all around. The women took over working at the presses as the war wore on, so that by the end of the five years of war, there were only a couple of older men and a few boys left working there, as they were either too old or too young to be called up to serve. When the war ended, the men were hired on and the women were asked to leave so that the returning bread-winners and war heroes could find work. And besides, women now had the role of creating a happy home and re-populating the country: this was the beginning of the Baby-boomer generation.

The significance of this building in my world was that the factory employed almost all the uncles in my family. This was in the days before human resources and qualifications. You literally walked in the door and if you looked the part and someone in the factory put in a good word for you, then you were given a job. To quote Mum, "It's not what you know, but who you know that gets you work."

The rooms in the factory were small and cramped, with the exception of one large room for the huge metal printing press. The storage rooms for the reams and reams of paper the factory used were also tiny. The floors were wooden and uneven and dirty from years of oil and print from the main press. The roof leaked, despite being patched with tar and some of the windows were still boarded up or had blackout tape on them from when there was a near-miss bombing during the war.

The sound of transistor radios could be heard throughout the workplace, as for the first time ever in history, everyone had access to individual musical choices. However, these mod cons did not extend to the toilet facilities. They were all outside—

indoor toilets were still a rarity in the early 1960s. The few women who now worked there with their bouffant hairstyles and tight skirts, complained bitterly about them. Only three women worked there now, doing what the men either could not or would not do. These were the typist, the filing clerk and of course the lady with the tea and snack trolley.

Uncle John and Uncle Ern (short for Ernest), were the two most senior workers at the factory and always the ones to make the final decisions. The war had put these men on a pedestal, but the power they held would consequently steer our family in a direction that changed all our lives forever. In their desperation for a better future, they would unwittingly leave behind something of great value, something they had taken for granted, something that once lost they would never be able to regain.

The still battle-scarred men were working at the factory; everyone was tired physically and mentally from the war and what they wanted more than anything was a bright future and to escape the horrors of the recent past. People wanted to move on, to leave the suffering and dying behind, a better tomorrow might somehow make all their losses justifiable. Tremendous sacrifices had been made during the war so that they could preserve their way of life. Surely, it was time now for this better future to happen. Surely, their families deserved a better standard of living with good housing, plenty of food, and good jobs for all.

I came home from school one day to the sound of angry

voices from the living room. Being a curious child, I headed in that direction and found Mum, Dad, Auntie, and Uncle together with Uncles John and Ernest sitting in our living room. Now one visiting uncle was normal but two together I had never heard of before.

As I bounced into the living room, the conversation stopped completely. They all looked so serious that I wondered if someone had died. The uncles were angry and I thought Mum's eyes looked a bit watery, as if she had been crying. Six pairs of eyes turned to look at me and Mum immediately got up and shooed me into my bedroom. This was apparently an adult secret family discussion.

Well, this had never happened before. I usually got to stay for at least a minute or two. Unfortunately, despite my best efforts to listen at the top of the stairs and work my way towards the living room before I was caught, the only words I could hear were something to do with 'new houses'.

As mentioned earlier, I am a nothing like the china doll that Mum was hoping for; I was a tomboy. I had short brown hair, very neat and tidy, but I did not wear trousers as only boys wore trousers in those days unless, of course, you were an older teenager who sometimes wore the latest fashion of a trouser suit. I was happy, although I still didn't quite feel that I fit in with my friend Judy of the 'bouncy ponytail' club and I was certainly not part of the *Bunty* comic stereotype that I read about every Saturday morning.

But today was Valentine's Day and since I really did not understand what the fuss was all about, I pretended that it was just a normal day. But deep down, I dreaded the day and so I reluctantly dragged myself into school to find the usual Valentine's nonsense going on.

Some of the boys and girls in my class exchanged small gifts to which the girls reacted with smiles and excitement. Judy and Terry were, of course, doing this, too, as they had been a couple for ages. They knew all about writing and giving cards and the little silly kisses written at the end of the message.

School eventually finished and our gang arranged to meet later on the doorstep of 11b. We sat on the steps chatting, except for Terry and Judy who were actually sitting so close together they were touching. Mum called to say that tea was ready and everyone stood up to go, when Anthony came over to me, his eyes looking down at a small square package he was holding. I stared at it and he quickly pushed it into my hand and rushed way. It was all very odd. I opened the little flap on the package and saw that inside were four tubes of Love Hearts sweets.

I had no idea why he was suddenly buying me sweets; I had my own pocket money from Mum and we went to Mrs. Williams' shop on Fridays to get them, so why was Anthony becoming my sweet supplier? That was Mum's job. How strange life was at times. Saying nothing, I turned to go into the house so that my tea would not get cold. At least there was nothing odd about that.

After tea, I looked at the sweet packet again and opened them. The small coin-shaped sweets each had a heart printed on them with the messages 'Love You', 'First Love', 'Kiss Me' and 'Call Me'. It was only after I had eaten a few, thinking that they tasted pretty good, that I realised Anthony had given me a Valentine, that he actually *liked* me!

I was still in shock the next day. I didn't know if I'd ever be able to look at Anthony again. It was a whole week before I could even meet his eyes, but I eventually got over the surprise that a boy could have feelings for me like grown-ups had. I thought you had to be a girly-girl like Judy with the flower-embroidered cardigan to have a boyfriend. But I wasn't like Judy and Anthony stilled liked me. It was peculiar.

Things were different at home too; Mum was in a strange mood. In fact, she had been a bit strange since my uncles' visit at that meeting about an adult family secret. She would usually clean the two whole flights of stairs once a week. Every Friday, I would come home from school and Mum would be halfway down the last flight of stairs on her hands and knees with a bucket by her side, cleaning the red vinyl. But this Friday, she was especially efficient in her cleaning, with water flying everywhere and the cleaning brush getting to every possible speck of dirt. I had learned through experience, under these circumstances, to make no comment and to become invisible. So I quietly crept past her up the stairs and disappeared into my bedroom.

Luckily for me, it was Friday—our fish and chip day—

which provided Mum with sufficient diversion to temporarily forget whatever was aggravating her. So after she finished her assault on the stairs, we went off to the fish and chip shop to get dinner.

Lamlash Street was very much like a small village. Within a five-minute walk, there were two corner shops, two fruit and vegetable shops, the sweet shop, and the fish and chip shop. We went in and queued up with the others; it always smelled of cooking fat, batter, and chips. There was a white marble counter with a large glass window in it. The fresh fish were on the other side and behind them were the deep-fat fryers. Mum, Dad, and my brother would have cod and chips and I had rock salmon and chips.

A lot of fish was eaten during the war, and post-war, that we might not consider eating now. Years later, I learned that rock salmon, which you can still buy in the UK, is actually a small shark! I absolutely loved my rock salmon with spicy HP brown sauce smothered over the top of the chips. They were always served in greaseproof paper wrapped inside a large piece of newspaper to make a warm bundle that smelled deliciously of chips and freshly cooked batter. I think the cost was 1/6d (1 shilling and sixpence) each.

Friday night was also sweet night and we would get 6 pence pocket money and go with Mum to Mrs. Williams' sweet shop. She was an elderly lady who wore a floral apron and she was assisted by a slightly younger woman. Her shop was in an ordinary Victorian house. You walked down the hallway and turned left into a converted room, which had a countertop with railings as a serving area for customers.

The amazing selection of sweets was stored in tall glass jars with screw tops. You would make your choice and Mrs. Williams would put them in a small white paper bag for you. The thin chocolate bars were 2 pence each and the 2 ounces of sweets in the bags were even cheaper. So for 6 pence you got a lot of sweets. My favourites included flying saucers and sherbet lemons but the best of all were the Love Hearts. In fact, as the year progressed, Love Hearts quickly became my favourite of all.

When we returned home with our food and treats, we all sat down around the dining room table. It was a strangely silent meal, with none of the usual chit chat; everyone stared into space as if something else was dominating their thoughts. I tried to be invisible and was on my very best behaviour. Sadly, my brother did not have this ability and after a minor transgression of getting tomato ketchup on his trousers, Mum snapped at him, bringing dinner to an abrupt halt. I began to understand that something of momentous importance was happening but couldn't imagine what it might be. I thought for a moment that it was money problems but I had been with Mum to the rent office that day to pay the rent as usual. I remembered staring at the fierce-looking, rent-collecting lady behind the iron bars and the dark wooden counter as Mum passed over the rent book with the money inside.

I was submerged in my own thoughts until, with some

relief, Auntie came upstairs to talk to Mum, leaving the rest of us to finish our dinner in peace. I was then told it was time for bed, which was a bit early, but to be honest I was glad to be in my bedroom and away from all the gloom surrounding the adults.

The next day, as on every Saturday morning, we were allowed to read our children's comics in bed until 11 o'clock. My comic was full of girls with perfect ponytails and skirts with petticoats; they would spend most of the story in their bedrooms listening to records or playing with their miniature poodle dogs. The most fascinating part for me was the cut-out doll on the back page. My brother's comic, on the other hand, was full of action, and guns, tanks, and cars, so I planned to read his comic later in the day as an antidote to the china-doll effect all around me.

While life was in one sense very predictable and following its usual rhythm, there seemed to be something worrying looming on the horizon as well.

CHAPTER 4

FIRST LOVE

First love is all about that connection with a living thing that we care so much about that just to be with them is all that we ask for. Just to see them makes us smile on the outside and the inside all at once; they are all you need. It's what true happiness is about and there is no need for anything else. When you see them, you feel that warm glow inside and you know that everything is right with the world, as long as you share your life with them.

All through my young life there had been pets. Mum believed that pets were important as they gave us a sense of responsibility, the idea of looking after something less able than ourselves. Now Auntie saw things slightly differently. To her, pets were something to love and cherish. So my road to first love started with Patch, the dog, then along came Titch, the cat, and in between there was Rosy, Dosy, and Nosy, the three short-lived baby chicks that Uncle brought back from the market one day, much to Mum's disgust.

Then there was Rex, the dog who lived with the family in the dingy basement flat. Rex was a mixed breed, Mum used to call him a 'liquorice allsorts' dog; he was part Labrador and part Retriever and was very friendly. I used to see him a lot when he was out with Lorraine. When she was busy, she let him visit me and I got to walk him on days when I needed a little love. Even though he wasn't my dog, whenever I had been told off, his pretty brown and white face made me feel a little better.

I now felt that at the age of 10 I had matured to the point that I was ready to move from my pets' love and focus more on boys. The incident on Valentine's Day had got me thinking about boys in a different way and that maybe one or two of them might even be nice to spend some time with. To be honest, there was only one boy that I really wanted to focus on and that was Anthony. My life felt good when I was with him. We talked a lot, and I was glad that he was part of my gang of friends.

What I liked about Anthony was that he was smart and good at schoolwork. He was a quiet person who liked to sit and talk about just about anything with me. He also dressed really well and so he met with Mum's approval, because as you remember, 'clothes maketh the man'.

At school, he used to send me little notes, not about love or anything silly like that, but about what he did that day and asking what had I been up to. What did I like, what did I hate; anything I said to him was okay. So, he wrote notes about his pet hamster Cyril, and I wrote about my latest Lego house. It was as if what we talked about wasn't so important, it was just a way to connect. To see that note from him made me smile inside because…I didn't really know why. There was no 'because', it just *was*. It was a warm and cosy feeling. Life was good and I was happy.

After school and during the school holidays, most of my time was spent playing out on the street with friends; it was very rare for friends to come inside the house, even if it was raining. Unless, of course, there was a birthday party. We basically stayed out of our parents' way and in our own little world away from them. Children's TV was only on for one hour a day, between 5 and 6 o'clock, and then the news came on, in which I had no interest. Without video games or electronics of any kind, if I wasn't playing outside on the streets, then I would read my books, which were mainly school-girl adventure novels and mysteries.

There was not that much traffic on Lamlash Street and the street was only wide enough for one car so it was a fairly safe place for kids. We would play ballgames, throwing balls up against the wall to hit the street sign, which would rattle as it was a metal sign in a lose wooden frame. That game was called 'Lamlash'. We also played 'marbles' which were glass-coloured beads; we would try to knock one another's marbles out of the circle. At other times, we would play 'jacks' with tiny metal six-point spiky pieces; you had to throw the ball in the air and pick up the metal pieces all with one hand before catching the ball. But mostly we would play ball and some hopscotch and skipping. We even got into the French skipping craze, which involved a large piece of elastic around the ankles of two people, who stood facing each other, while a third person jumped over the elastic backwards and forwards in a variety of ways. Our other pastime was to hang upside down by our legs from metal bars only three feet from the ground, outside the neighbour's front door, and pretend that we were trapeze artists.

And then there was my bike, which I would ride around the streets in the middle of London traffic for hours, with no thought of it being dangerous. It was completely normal for a 10-year-old to ride in the middle of London traffic with no helmet for protection.

The bomb sites were also our playgrounds and I would ride in and out of the ruins and up and down the hills and dirt paths of the demolished houses that had been bombed during WWII, like I was on a BMX adventure track. The houses were not yet rebuilt, or for that matter even fully demolished. There were half-standing brick walls with weeds and plants starting to grow in them. There were rats the size of cats and other sorts of vermin everywhere, and everyone knew to always keep an eye out for the rats while playing and avoid them.

One day, china doll met tomboy, with disastrous results. I was in a hurry to join the gang who were going to bike and hadn't changed out of my brand-new clothing, which consisted of a pink silk blouse with matching scarf attached and a brown tartan skirt. I had just finished riding a particularly exciting set of hills when one of the boys decided to pull on my pink scarf. Well, this ripped off half the buttons on the blouse and the scarf detached completely. It was a real nuisance as I had to stop riding my bike and head back to the house to face Mum and the consequences. She didn't understand how I could be so careless and promptly marched me off to my bedroom as a punishment, with orders to get ready for bed early!

As I mentioned earlier, there were five of us in our gang, three girls and two boys. We were in the 'better off' group of kids, shall we say; we stayed away from the kids in our class who slept in their day clothes and would come to school smelling because they didn't wash either themselves or their clothes. It didn't occur to us that they probably had no bath or washing machine in the house. So, if there were no adults to handwash their clothes or take them to the local public baths, they really had no way of keeping clean. But being kids and totally unaware of these social issues, we pretty much ignored them and considered them unworthy of our time.

Even within our working-class community, there was still a pecking order. I mixed with the nicer kids in the area, not those who dressed badly. My group of friends had a little more money for clothes and went on holiday every year. When we went on holiday, Mum made sure that it was always to the more expensive holiday camps, now known as resorts. The chalets that we stayed in were slightly better quality and were larger than the cheaper holiday camps. The entertainment was slightly better, with more paid entertainers and fewer amateur talent shows, which Mum had a hatred of. We had Blue Coat holiday staff looking after us, not the basic Red Coat entertainment staff of the other, slightly inferior, holiday camps. Well, that's how Mum saw it, and Mum's standards were the gold standard for the family.

The other person I would spend time with outside of our gang was Susan across the road. She was a few years older than me, a simple person, but she liked to play the Lamlash ballgames too. I also used to join Susan for Sunday school at the London Tabernacle.

The Metropolitan Tabernacle was founded by preacher Charles Haddon Spurgeon in the nineteenth century. The church was on the same grounds where martyrs were burned for their religious beliefs a few hundred years earlier. They were both Catholic and Protestant martyrs, depending upon the legally prevailing religion of the time. None of this was horrifying or really bothered me or anyone else I knew, as death was just part of life, for not only the martyrs but also my family in the recent war. As Mum always said, there is no point in sugar-coating life events, you are just as well to call 'a spade and spade' and not a shovel.

I must have been the only child on the street who went to church without my parents encouraging me to go. But I learned new things there, and the people were friendly and ran programs for kids. So why would a Church of England-baptised, 10-year-old girl, a Girl Guide who always joined the church parade at St Jude's Church, attend a Reformed Baptist Church? That was easy; the Tabernacle welcomed all children and even when we attended the main church, I still felt welcomed and not a nuisance. In contrast, St Jude's was unwelcoming and full of people who saw children as something only to be tolerated.

During the school summer holidays, the Tabernacle held an afternoon religious and craft school for children, which I loved. They even gave me a book for good attendance, *The Coconut Island Twins*. I can't recall any such incentive from St. Jude's.

My world was perfect the way it was; it met all my needs and it was predictably comforting. What I did not foresee was that my needs were very subtly changing as were the needs of those around me—and that would change everything.

But back to my first love. One day, when our little gang met on the doorstep of 11b, Anthony and I were sitting near one another as usual when I quietly moved up right next to him. I don't know why I did it but it just seemed like a normal thing to do. He then leaned forward and kissed me on my right cheek, which I thought would have felt odd because, well, nobody from school had ever kissed me before and certainly not an icky boy; but this somehow felt nice and warm, and friendly, and so safe.

Of course, the rest of the gang noticed immediately and so Terry and Judy, being the 'experienced' hand-holding couple, said that by way of a public declaration Anthony and I should kiss on the lips in front of everyone to seal our relationship. The thought seemed strange to me on the one hand, and unnatural, but I knew that this is what grown-ups did and since I had an official boyfriend it seemed reasonable.

So after what seemed like forever of being 'dared' to kiss in front of everyone, Anthony slowly puckered his way towards me. Honestly, I was more interested in hand holding. It was all just a bit embarrassing, really.

A split second before the kiss there came a loud banging noise from the window upstairs. It was my eagle-eyed mother, who had been watching the unfurling romance and yelled at me that it was time for me to come in for tea. That was the end of the first romantic interlude in my life and I didn't even get a kiss. I didn't think it would bother me at all…but it did.

After my 'almost kiss' Mum kept a close eye on me. The next day, she told me that we would visit Nan, who was Dad's mum. So Mum, my brother, and I all duly climbed aboard the number 63 bus to Farringdon Road.

Nan lived in a block of flats that were built of stone and dated back to the Victorian times. She was on the fourth floor but there was no lift as the flats had been built for the working poor. Nan lived with a very nice man named Arthur who always wore a suit and tie. He was a thin, fragile-looking man who was very quiet; except for Christmas time when he played the spoons. It never occurred to me to ask why Arthur was not called Grandad; he was always just known as Arthur.

The flat had a tiny kitchen but no bathroom, as no one had a bathroom back then. It did, however, have the luxury of an indoor toilet. There was also a living room with lots of dark furniture. I remember being fascinated by the Dry Sack lady ornament on the sideboard. Arthur worked for the Dry Sack sherry company, and so there was a Dry Sack ashtray and a couple of bottles of sherry there, too, all wrapped up in bottle-sized real little sacks. Next door was the bedroom where Nan allowed me to look through her jewellery box and play with some of her rings.

A visit to Nan's always included a trip for me and my brother along the landing to visit Mrs. Smith, an old lady who lived alone. Mrs. Smith wore a hairnet, sensible leather lace-up shoes, thick stockings, a loose-fitting cardigan, and a skirt that almost covered her legs to her ankles. The flat was dark and in the dining room was a heavy wooden table covered in a brown chenille tablecloth. She had a large jar of wrapped boiled sweets and we were allowed to choose three sweets each from it. Sometimes she would have the sweets with the chocolate middles; I always chose those when she had them as they were extra tasty.

As a 10-year-old, to me, Nan was a very proper lady, but as I said earlier, in her youth she had been a little more co-lourful. Back then, after Nan paid a trip to the pub, it was not unusual for my dad to return home to find a different 'uncle' staying the night. Before you judge you should consider how difficult her life was—raising two boys alone having given one away, living with no social safety net, and making ends meet by doing grueling physical work pushing carriages on the railway.

I later learned that Nan did not divorce the violent man

she had married when she was barely 20, which is why she never married Arthur. She did, however, marry Charlie when she was in her sixties, after her husband and Arthur had both died. Maybe she was just a lady doing her best, trying to survive, and was not trying to be colourful in any way.

Speaking of trying to survive, I finally found out what had caused the atmosphere of doom and gloom among the adults. It was the factory; Uncle told me that the business might move to a different part of England. He explained that negotiations were underway and that the new factory location would be a better, cleaner, and safer place for the workers. He said that there was a lot of opposition and grumbling about doing this to former soldiers who made such sacrifices during the war. But he said it made sense, too, since the current building was in a horrible state and for all anyone knew it was likely to be condemned due to the nearby bomb strikes that had weakened the walls. This meant that the uncles would be out of work if they did not relocate with the factory. It was a very upsetting prospect for everyone as they would have to leave London and go to a place that they did not know. When you consider that most families only had one income (the man's), it was obvious that the adults had very little choice: Either relocate or starve. It was Hobson's Choice—no choice really at all.

It was a shock but I tried to look on the bright side—as Dad was soon to be a black cabbie after he passed his last appearances, it would not really affect us. We would be able to stay on Lamlash Street.

Mum, an independently minded woman and a keen organiser of anything around the family home, couldn't be involved in the factory issues or control the outcome for anyone as she was a woman and this was firmly male territory. This uncomfortably frustrating place for her to be could lead to only one thing: Cleaning and decorating on a massive scale, and me keeping my head low. She was always a stickler for keeping the house spotless and this included the large bay windows. During the sixties, pollution from coal burning was a health hazard, as the air was full of dirt and soot, and the windows of the house were always grimy. We had to burn coke as the smokeless coal was known, which was cheaper to buy than coal and the only fuel we were allowed to use in the fireplace. Mum said that it was the law that we could not burn coal because of the terrible London smog that had happened a few years earlier.

To clean the windows at 11b, Mum would sit on the top floor window ledge four floors up, her legs hanging over the edge, using a bucket and chammy (chamois) leather to wash and dry the windows on both the inside and the outside. She had no safety harness or even anyone to help her; it was just Mum performing this dare-devil act, oblivious to the danger, to keep the windows nice and clean.

Mum also did the wallpapering. In fact, we would always decorate the house together as a result of which I am now pretty good at hanging wallpaper, which is a dying art. As part of her destressing campaign, Mum decided to wallpaper my bedroom. Rolls of wallpaper in those days came with a perforated edge, a bit like the old dot matrix printer paper that you had to tear off before using. The technique for removing this perforated edge was to hit the edge of the paper against something solid. Mum tried a few times but without success so she thought she would try it against the sturdy-looking mantelpiece. Well, it worked, the edge did come off but so did a large corner piece of the mantle…it broke off in a large chunk! After some thought, Mum got some Sellotape (sticky tape) and somehow reattached it. She then painted the whole mantle white and swore me to secrecy, which made me feel really important, and no one else was ever the wiser.

My bedroom was next to my brother's on the top floor of the house. My brother's room always had a bucket in the middle of the floor to catch the drips from the ceiling. Every time it rained, the water would trickle through the hole made in the celling so that the whole thing did not collapse. But Mum tried to make the bedrooms warm, they always had a rose-coloured glow from the pink light bulb in the electric convector heater. I'm not sure if the heater produced much actual warmth; I think the pink bulb just gave an illusion of heat, as the rooms were always cold. However, Mum always made sure that we had a nice warm bed with hot water bottles and lots of heavy blankets.

The only indoor toilet was one floor down at the back of the house, which it was decided was too far for us to get to at night. We were, therefore, given chamber pots to pee in overnight. We kept them under our beds. Mine was pink plastic. Some mornings if I was careless, I would knock the side of it and get cold pee on my foot but this was just part of normal life and other than getting a wet foot and having to wipe it on the sheets, it had no more significance than that.

I sometimes wondered at how hard Mum worked at maintaining our house and if there were other crises hovering in the background that I didn't know about. I also wondered how much more cleaning it was going to take for her to get back to normal. Around this time something else also changed in Uncle. My first thoughts were that he had heard about my confusing love life or that he was worried about the factory closing down. I was not sure why but suddenly Uncle felt a little more open to talking about his past.

It so happened that I had homework to do about WWII and wanted to ask Dad if he had any stories, but Dad was working long hours now he was a cabbie and so I rarely saw him as he always finished work after my bedtime.

Uncle had always stared off into space whenever I brought up the war so I was wary about raising it with him. In fact, I'd sometimes catch him staring at bomb sites in our neighbourhood with a pained and distant expression on his face. But since I had to get this homework done or suffer the consequences from Mr. Chapel, I went ahead and asked Uncle about the Merchant Navy. I told him how important it was to me as it was schoolwork and much to my relief, he, with some hesitation, started to talk and told me one of his war stories.

He told me about the time when he was ready to leave

for war and his Dad took him round to the local pub for a last drink. He said it was bad enough for his Dad to send him off to war and watch his son put himself in danger. He had after all raised Uncle for 17 years during which time he knew who Uncle was with and what he was doing; but then he had to let him go to places where people were dying and his Dad knew that he may never see his son again; this was horrifying for them both.

Uncle found it ironic that although he was old enough to die for his country, he wasn't yet old enough to legally drink. In the pub, his father gave him some man-to-man advice: 'Don't drink any alcohol, only grapefruit juice; don't smoke; and don't disgrace your name with bad women.' They had just finished laughing about how to tell a bad woman from a good one, when an older lady approached him. She quietly put something in Uncle's jacket pocket. He grabbed her hand. It was an envelope. Uncle opened it to find a white feather, the sign of a coward. This was one of the most insulting things that you could say to a man during the war and Uncle was deeply hurt. The woman viciously demanded to know why he was not in uniform and serving in the forces. She said, 'My two sons are serving now. While you are here safe and warm, they are fighting on the front. How dare you show your face in this pub! You are a coward and everyone should know it!'

Uncle could see his father's eyes fill with anger and they both tried to keep their feelings in check. Uncle told me it took every ounce of control he had to proudly and calmly reply, 'This silver badge with the initials M and N is my uniform.

I am in the Merchant Navy, and just having a last drink with my dad before I go off to serve my country.'

The woman replied, quickly, 'So sorry, young man, my anger got the better of me. Let me buy you a drink to make amends.'

In the dark days of war, families would see their children—sons especially—go off to fight and many, many did not come back. You need to remember that this was the second time in two generations that lives had been lost to war. It had a devastating impact on whole families. So you can begin to understand how conscientious objectors were vilified and hated because they were still alive while the war heroes were lost forever.

This was one of the few occasions in his life when Uncle was so angry that he was rude to a person and in particular a lady. His anger eventually got the better of him and he shouted at her, 'Get out of my sight!'

He then turned to his dad who was still upset and said, 'Let's have another drink, and this time I will have a beer!' With their beers in their hands his dad proposed a toast: 'Take good care of yourself, son, and come home safe to your mother and me.'

Uncle had told me this story without much emotion to save my young feelings, but years later he would say that he still felt pain from the experience. This wouldn't be the last time that Uncle shared with me what he had been through.

CHAPTER 5

CHARLOTTE SHARMAN

My own exclusive world, in which Mum's influence was minimal, was my school. Charlotte Sharman Primary school, in West Square was named after a Christian woman who ran orphanages for girls in the late nineteenth and early twentieth centuries. She took in orphaned girls who were destined for the workhouse and a future of child slavery. She fed and clothed them and gave them an education in home and domestic training. Her orphanage in Southwark was a stone's throw from my school. Of course, I had no idea of the philanthropy behind it when I attended the school itself.

The school was a large brick-built building on two floors with Bedlam Park on one side and West Square on the other. And a certain boy running around the corridors who had completely confused my life. My head tried to make sense of these emotions but I didn't understand them. In my well-ordered and organised life, confusion had settled in and no matter how hard I tried, I could not make sense of it. Life was now unpredictable and I did not like it.

I was considered old enough to get to and from school by myself. The 10-minute route took me along Hayles Street and St. Georges Road, which was the Mum-approved safer but longer route. If I was late, I would take the unapproved shortcut through an alleyway called Fives Court. It was a tall, dark, and narrow alleyway, a very dingy place with lots of twists and turns, and would not have been out of place in a scene from the old movie *Gaslight*. You could just imagine Jack the Ripper waiting around the next corner of those blackened 20-foot high walls. There was only one street light about half-way along, which barely provided any light at all. The reality to me was that this 'cut-through', as it was known, reduced the walking time by at least five minutes so on those days when I was running late, this was the route I took. Also, since none of my class had ever been attacked in this alleyway, but several of them *had* been caned by the teacher for being late, it seemed to me that a potential Jack the Ripper attack was far less likely than being caned by an angry teacher.

Talking of angry teachers, my biggest concerns at school were Miss Reynolds, the headmistress, and Mr. Chapel, the assistant head. Miss Reynolds was a pleasant enough lady with a short, conservative haircut, who wore a tweed suit with sensible flat shoes. I was called to her office once or twice about some transgression although I can't recall now what it was all about. My real concern, however, was Mr. Chapel, who was not only the assistant headmaster but also my class teacher.

On an ordinary day at school, I would be sitting at my desk while Mr. Chapel walked up and down the rows looking at our work, when suddenly he would tap a boy on the shoulder and bring him out in front of the class for some wrongdoing and cane him. This was in the day when corporal punishment in school was endorsed, when inappropriate behaviour was corrected by hitting children with a stick that we called the cane. It was not unusual for the boys (and it was always the boys) to be punished in this way. The boys said that what was worse than actually getting the cane, was the fear of being seen crying by your classmates, after the punishment.

It seemed to me that Mr. Chapel was the only teacher who caned boys, as the other teachers would 'only' give an occasional rap on the knuckles with a ruler, which to us somehow seemed less serious. He was a very tall and intimidating man, who always wore a suit and tie to school. There was no explanation or reason for the punishment that I could understand, and since school was a dictatorship and not a democracy, the teacher felt fully justified in his actions.

The impact of this violence on us as children was not considered. It was, however, a powerful motivator to say nothing, to do your schoolwork, and above all keep quiet, especially when he was around. One day, Mum gave me a bottle of wine for him, which I duly delivered. This was in the days when only the 'well-to-do' drank wine. I am not sure why she did this but I assumed it was to keep on his good side and me out of his sights, which was just fine by me.

School wasn't the only place where we were hit. Hitting pupils' knuckles with a stick was even acceptable to my piano teacher. If I had not done my homework to her expected level then my hands were hit as punishment while I was practising. After a few weeks of this, I told Mum that I wasn't interested in piano lessons any more. If I had told her that I was being hit because I did not do my homework, she would have insisted that I keep going to the lessons. The Victorian phrase that adults would use to justify corporal punishment was 'spare the rod and spoil the child', which meant that if you did not punish the child with violence, the child would grow to become a spoilt individual. It was a belief much supported by almost any adult—hitting a child with the back of a wooden spoon as a means of correcting poor behaviour was encouraged. I did not even think to question it. I was too busy avoiding any unwanted attention, and since all the children I knew were subject to the same rules, I considered it just a normal part of life.

Something else far more serious had been bothering me: The thought of Anthony and the almost-kiss. I realised it was another form of punishment—regret—and decided that regardless of what else happened I would kiss Anthony on the lips. I just had no idea how to make that happen. Then it came to me: the answer was a telephone.

It was Mum's idea that we have a telephone—we always had the upgraded version of any gadgets of the day, all the mod cons. I think that now we would call Mum an early adopter. Our newest piece of technology was the telephone, which had been installed a year earlier. It was a large black heavy thing with a cute little pull-out drawer for addresses at the bottom. I thought it would be easier for me to ask Anthony for a kiss if I did not have to look at him. It seemed to me that calling him up on the telephone was the obvious answer.

One day, I asked Mum if I could use it. Well, that was the wrong thing to say! The floodgates opened up and she said in no uncertain terms that the telephone was strictly for adult use, as calls were charged by the minute, and did I think we were made of money? She said that only important adult things were to be discussed on the telephone and a mere child had no place using one!

Now, it seemed to me that in reality the telephone was hardly ever used. Dad didn't like talking on it; I only ever saw him use it once when Mum instructed him to speak to one of his relatives who lived in Kineton, Warwickshire, which is about 80 miles outside London. So that was a very firm 'no'. I would have to find another way of getting my kiss.

I was still thinking about the romantic side of my ever-changing life one day when I was chatting with Auntie. She asked me about my special friend, Anthony. I told her that he was nice and we liked talking together.

Since we were on the subject of romance, I thought I would ask Auntie how she and Uncle met. She was a bit guarded at first, but I managed to glean that she was in a pub with her sister, my mum, when she spotted a tall, good-looking man in the other section of the pub. Now Uncle had the gift of the gab and would talk for hours with a twinkle in his eye and a pint in his hand. He came over to the two young ladies and used his charm to ask Auntie out.

As I said earlier, their father was a regimental sergeant major and before any of his daughters were courted the young man had to ask his permission. If it was not granted, the brothers would pay the would-be suitor a visit and explain in no uncertain terms that he was not welcome. Grandad was 6' tall and of an impressive build; his sons were also between 5' 11" and 6' 2" tall, and there were six of them so the intimidation factor was high. Uncle duly asked for permission to date Auntie, but there were strict rules. Auntie had to be back home by 11 o'clock; Uncle had to look after her and was entirely responsible for her welfare during the time they were out, 'no ifs, ands or buts'. If these rules were not met, then she wouldn't be able to see him again. Obviously, Uncle met the standards required and they were married for 47 very happy years.

As for my plan to get Anthony to kiss me, I was stumped. I wished I could just ask, but only boys could ask for a kiss; girls were seen as too easy if they made the first move. This was so unfair and annoying, but I supposed that if I wanted to have a grown-up relationship, I had to do it the grown-up way. Then one day at school, Anthony passed a note to me in the playground when I was with some of my girl classmates. It was the usual note about nothing significant, just this and that, except at the end of the note was a tiny little 'x', just one little extra letter.

I missed it at first and then later re-read the note and there it was, 'Anthony x'. But what did it mean? Other than the almost-kiss brought to an abrupt end by Mum and the Love Hearts on Valentine's Day, there really had been none of that stuff. But here it sat, this tiny little 'x', which somehow seemed to have some massive significance. Or did it?

Was I a highly perceptive 10-year-old reading something into this that was real or was I overreacting to this tiny little taunting 'x'? Was this a message about undying love or was it just a sign of a deepening friendship? Was he saying I think you are a great friend or was he saying you are the one forever? Even more of a worry was, how should I respond?

It seemed to me that this 'boyfriend' business was a lot more complicated than I'd thought. I really wanted to just walk up to him and ask him what this meant, but somehow it did not feel like the mature thing to do, as though I should somehow know what the intention behind the 'x' was. I could just ignore it and pretend it never happened but then he obviously liked me so that did not seem the right thing to do either.

I thought about it for that whole week but still hadn't come up with a plan. I considered asking Judy's advice but decided she would laugh at me. Then quite suddenly, Anthony stopped talking to me; he stopped the funny comments and the little notes about Cyril. I didn't understand why. I really liked things the way they were. Why did he have to go and spoil things with that little 'x'?

As I was feeling a complete disaster in the romance department, I thought I would go and see the one person who might be keen to talk about a subject as far away from romance as I could get.

I went off to look for Uncle and ask about more of his war adventures. I discovered him sitting in the living room, a pint in his hand. I asked him what had happened after the white feather incident in the pub so he told me about the time he reported for Merchant Navy orientation at Dock Street in Aldgate. This was the base for the Merchant Navy—different from the Royal Navy, which was known as the Senior Service. Uncle described the Royal Navy as the upper class and the Merchant Navy as second best, even though the men of both services equally put their lives on the line every day.

Uncle reported for orientation on board a war ship moored at the Embankment area of the River Thames. In his very first week of service, he learned how to row, use a compass, tie nautical knots, and rudimentary seamanship. He even showed me the notes he took on a government-issued reporter's notebook 'ruled with feint lines'.

He was taught the names of parts of the ship, such as forward, port, starboard, forecastle, midships, and stern; he also learned about the supplies onboard a lifeboat, of which there were apparently 33, amongst which were axes, an oil bag, a tripping line (whatever that may be), and a two-gallon bucket for bailing water, should things not go well.

He had copious notes on the 32 compass points but admitted that he really only recalled North, South, East, and West. Finally, they got to the information that he'd been waiting for—all about the boiler room, his new home to be. But although he had 10 pages of notes there was not one word about the role of 'trimmer', the position he'd been hired for.

In the second week of training, this 17-year-old reported to Shoeburyness, near Essex and the mouth of the Thames Estuary, for gunnery training. A target was dropped by parachute and the men fired upon it with rifles. He also learned how to dismantle and reassemble a Lewis gun, which is a machine gun.

In his third week of what developed into a baptism of smoke *and* fire, he was repeatedly instructed to enter a smoke-filled hut and identify the odour. This frequently caused his eyes to water and irritated his lungs, making him cough. He was then asked what he thought the smoking item was. There were no medical personnel available back then or concerns about toxic smoke; the philosophy was that you did this for the love of your country. Also, health and safety regulations were nonexistent so you were pretty much left to your own instincts.

He did tell me, though, that the threat of England being invaded was constant and that he would do anything to defend his loved ones and their way of life. This was in some ways a very personal war; he was doing it to protect his mum and dad and family. If for a second he forgot this, then the Doodlebugs over London every night during the Blitz, destroying his city and killing his neighbours, were constant reminders.

On Lamlash Street, the neighbourhood was up in arms at news of the factory being relocated somewhere outside London. Uncles Ern and John were at the house again. This time I did not go into the living room but sat outside, just close enough to hear at least a little of what was being discussed. Uncle John said that they had met with the owners of the factory and told them that they were putting a whole neighbourhood out of work and that families would starve if they had no money coming in. He said that they were trying to convince the owners to keep at least part of the factory open so that a few jobs would remain. Uncle Ern said, angrily, that the time had come for walkouts in protest of how the men were being treated, as time was moving on and there was still no sign of any job security. At this point, Mum announced it was time for a cup of tea, and I ran downstairs so as not to be caught as she headed towards the door.

You should understand that this is not, however, the usual story of cold profiteers ruining the lives of the working class. The factory owners knew that these men had fought in the war. They didn't want to disrupt the lives of an entire neighbourhood, but the sad reality was that the neighbourhood was already dead. People were living in condemned homes; the bombs had wiped out some buildings at the time, but it was as if the war was still going on as existing buildings were still not safe. The Marshall Plan (or European Recovery Plan) was an American initiative passed in 1948 for foreign aid to

Western Europe. It had provided some financial help to the UK in 1948 to rebuild the country but the reality was that even years later in the 1960s there was a housing crisis in cities that had been heavily bombed and still not enough money to replace all the homes that had been lost. Consequently, many people were still living in condemned housing, including all of us at 11b, which had already been condemned before we had moved into it.

Uncle questioned out loud what would happen to the business and the jobs if the factory building was condemned or even collapsed. The response from the owners and senior staff was that there may be more room for thought on the matter and there would be further discussions, but realistically, everyone knew that even if there was a delay in the factory move, it would happen someday.

So not only was my romantic life in turmoil but so were the lives of the adults. It seemed to me that, suddenly, life was pretty dismal all round. The only stable, predictable thing seemed to be the day-to-day running of the house, an arena that Mum completely controlled.

CHAPTER 6

THE HOUSEHOLD

Even with all this uncertainty, there was still a definite pattern to life at Lamlash, which to me was both comforting and reassuring. At the helm of this predictability was Mum. I knew that certain days of the week had special significance. Friday was clean the house day and a trip to Mrs. Williams' for sweets followed by a fish and chip tea. Saturday was lie in bed late and read comics day. Sunday was a big roast dinner, then Sunday school, followed later by a seafood tea and Disney's *Wonderful World of Colour* (ironically watched on a black and white TV). Monday was always laundry day, sandwiches for lunch, and bubble and squeak (fried leftovers from Sunday's roast dinner) for tea.

Mum's opinion was that a woman's role in life was to 'run' the household. This meant that wives and mothers would cook, clean, organise, and create a happy home for the husband and children. This involved devoting all of her time to washing and cooking, shopping and cleaning, and taking care of the children. A man's role was to provide the income for all this to take place, what was known as being the breadwinner. As I was a somewhat miniature woman, it was my lot in life to learn the 'skills' of running a home—that is when I was not at school working on my education.

I spent a lot of time in the kitchen with Mum, being surreptitiously schooled about how to cook vegetables, how to wash pots, and how to work the oven. I would also spend the whole of Monday during school holidays being taught the finer points of operating our Empress washing machine, which had the latest gadget: An electric mangle. No hand-cranking of the mangle for us! My brother, on the other hand, was free to just play and did not need these 'skills' to survive in life as we knew it in the 1960s.

I was also schooled in the virtues of Tupperware, that mouse-proof, modern-day product, which allowed us to put food in the cupboard by the oven without the mice taking their tithe. I was adept at using the electric cooker and knew about its delayed heating of the pots and pans as opposed to gas, which was so much quicker. I knew how to wash our black and white willow pattern dishes and how to clean lino and carpets. I would help to polish the linoleum in my room by tying yellow dusters on my feet and pretending that I was ice skating on the pink polished linoleum. My skills were endless!

One of the things that made running a home so labour intensive was the plumbing situation...or to be more precise the lack of plumbing. None of our neighbours or friends had a bathroom; one of my schoolmates had a bath in the kitchen with a wooden cover, which was used for the family's weekly bath. The toilet was usually an outhouse in the garden, which meant that at night you would go outside in the dark with your nightdress on. There were spiders in the corners and moths flying round the one dim bare lightbulb, and it was always dark and cold and scary. We, of course, had an inside toilet, which was insect-free.

Only a few housewives had a washing machine on our street, and most clothes were washed in the sink with a scrubbing board. Everyone wore their clothes multiple times to keep washing to a minimum, and it was a terrible sin if a child got their clothes dirty. Bedsheets were washed every fortnight, and the woolen blankets and feather-filled eiderdowns would never be cleaned but would be given the occasional airing on the washing line. Pillows were never washed either and were often decades old and full of dead skin cells and bed insects. The rule in those days was that if it looked clean, then it was clean, and well, a little bit of dirt never really hurt anyone, did it?

In our house, we had a tin bath hung very proudly on the back of the kitchen door. Every Saturday evening, Mum would turn the kitchen into a temporary bathroom. It was a real status symbol to be able to have a bath at home and to not have to go to the public baths. Remember, Mum always strived for our family to have a little more than the average.

For us, bath days were just once a week so for the remainder of the week, you would have a 'top and tail' wash with the flannel cloth and water at the sink. Nobody had a shower; it was a strange thing that you saw in American films. You have to understand that these were the days when no one we knew even traveled outside England, and a place like America with all its modern labour-saving devices was considered as far away as Mars is to us now.

Our nearest public place to take a bath was at Manor Place, a large Victorian building, so it, too, was at least a hundred years old. Inside on the top floor was a big swimming pool where we had school swimming lessons, and on the ground floor were rows and rows of private bathrooms and some steam rooms as well. The whole place was covered in shiny white and green tiles from top to bottom. You paid 2 pence for a bath of lukewarm water, which was the standard rate, and 5 pence for hot water, which came with a free top-up! Towels and carbolic soap were included in the price; carbolic soap was used as it killed off the lice. If you wanted a more delicate soap, then you could pay extra for Fairy soap. Even in those days there was upselling!

Most men's work in those days was dirty and very physical. Men would use the baths throughout the week, often before going home to eat the meal that was waiting for them. Saturday mornings were for women to use the baths while the men stayed at home to look after the children.

In our house every Saturday night, Mum would put the three-sectioned clothes horse around the tin bath and place sheets over the sections for privacy and warmth. The bath would then be filled with hot water, bucket by bucket, from the gas geyser over the kitchen sink. The geyser was a wall-hung, gas-fired water heater; you could hear the whoosh of the gas as it ignited and see the blue flames at the bottom. It was a fearsome-looking thing. The heat on the two 'bar' electric fire would be turned onto full power; the electric fire had a fan over the red-light bulb to give the impression of a flickering flame.

In our family, it was only my brother, Paul, and I who shared the bath water. I would be first in because, generally, I was cleaner than my brother. I had no idea how Mum and Dad bathed and being just a child, I had no right to know about these adult matters. In some other families, the whole family would take it in turn to wash in the same bath of water, with the smallest child going in first, then the next oldest child, and lastly the mum, followed by the dad. By the time the dad had bathed the water was pretty grimy, with scum floating on the top of the water. But as our family was always one better, only me and Paul would bathe in the same water. Afterwards, Mum would laboriously empty the bath, scooping out dirty water bucket by bucket, carrying it across the kitchen, and emptying it down the kitchen sink.

Warm towels were always waiting for us after the bath and our skin would be briskly rubbed dry. Our hair would be tow-eled until almost dry and then Mum dressed us in our clean pyjamas and we were bundled off to bed with a hot water bottle. I loved bath nights as everything was so warm and clean. On Sunday, we would wear our special church only clothes;

these were clothes that were not worn for the rest of the week. As we put on these special clothes, Mum would always remind us that 'cleanliness is next to Godliness'.

On the subject of Godliness, children in some other families were always sent to Sunday school on Sunday afternoon, but this had little to do with Christian education. Rents were very high after the war because of the housing shortage caused by the destruction of whole blocks of homes. Some families with less income than us lived in very crowded conditions, with just one bedroom for the whole family. There was barely enough money to pay for food, rent, and electricity and so couples certainly didn't have money for entertainment. While the children were packed off to Sunday school, parents would spend the afternoon in bed together, with the church acting as a babysitter.

Not all families in our neighbourhood were as fastidiously clean as ours, and so at school another regular occurrence was a visit from Nitty Nora. She was a lady who would check us for nits or more correctly, head lice. We would be taken out of class and instructed to form a line in the cloakroom where our coats were hung, then a lady in a stiff white lab coat would comb through our hair, one child at a time, looking for nits.

So this day, the whole class was assembled and, of course, this included the love of my life, Anthony. He was waiting in the queue a little bit behind me. As he tried to step nearer to me, I moved away. I could not bear the thought of him standing next to me if it came to my turn and Nitty Nora pointed her finger at me screaming 'LICE!' Now she didn't exactly scream lice but that was the way I feared it might go. And what if Anthony had lice? I would not be able to deal with that either.

There would usually be three or four kids that had nits. They were the ones we avoided anyway because they smelled and had holes in their dirty clothes. I tried to move further away from Anthony so that if I did have them, he might not hear Nitty Nora say so, but the ever-watchful teacher moved me back again and so I felt doomed.

Now there was never any discussion at home about having nits, about how to avoid them, or even what they were. I think that it was such a common occurrence—no more of an issue than catching a cold is today. You certainly didn't want them but they were just part of life—except for when you were standing near your boyfriend...then it was very different.

My turn came and I held my breath while Nitty Nora raked the comb through my hair; I felt a sense of dread. I thought of all the excuses I could come up with if a nit was found. So I crossed my fingers and prayed. Whether it was the praying or crossing my fingers that worked—or just luck—I don't know but mercifully I was nit-free! Now it was Anthony's turn. I held my breath again; what would I say to him if he had headlice? Would it ruin our friendship? Should I ask him how his nits were doing instead of asking about his hamster, Cyril, or just pretend he had none?

Thankfully he, too, was nit-free; we could put the whole episode behind us and just focus on swimming lessons the next day. You see you had to be nit-free to be able to swim at the baths.

While the visit by Nitty Nora was a necessary evil, the swimming lessons were something that I really enjoyed. These took place at Manor Place Baths, which was a 20-minute walk from school. Summer or winter alike, the whole class would walk in a long line along the back streets of Walworth Road to reach the baths. On the return trip, our hair was always damp because we had no hairdryers at the pool, but somehow we managed to survive the dangerous combination of wet hair and cold weather that my mother equated with certain death.

The swimming pool on the top floor of the building had changing rooms on either side. Upon reaching the poolside, we were duly assigned; two classmates to each small changing room, which meant that I had to change into my swimsuit with another girl in the same cramped space. Now since I carried a few extra pounds and did not like undressing in front of other skinny girls, we tried as much as possible to arrange these pairings so that we shared with a friend who would not make any comments, preferably one who also carried a few extra pounds. The boys were on the other side of the pool grappling with the same fate.

We all began learning how to swim at the shallow end of the pool, where your feet could touch the bottom, trying to swim the 25 yards across the width of the pool. If you could do that you were promoted to the next level and then had the dubious pleasure of seeing how far you could swim along the edge of the pool.

The swimming instructor's method of teaching was basic but very effective. The emphasis was on how long you could stay afloat while moving your arms and paddling your legs. The type of stroke used or any technique was irrelevant. The instructor, who was always dressed in her ordinary day clothes and brown brogue lace-up shoes, had absolutely no intention of jumping into the pool to rescue you if you were drowning. In fact, in the years that we visited the baths she was never once seen in the water and I have no idea if she could even swim because all she ever did was walk along the side of the pool with the wooden broom handle as our 'swimming aid'. As we attempted to swim around the edge of the pool, she would hold the broom handle just out of reach and if she thought you were starting to sink, she would bring the handle close enough for you to grab onto it. The one time I did reach for it when I felt I was sinking, she moved the broom handle just back out of my reach and ordered me to keep going, which I anxiously complied with. It was a very effective technique.

None of the children were given any type of floatation device. No arm bands were available, just the broom handle and your will to live. I think the adrenaline pumping through my system kept me alert and focused on that 1-inch thick stick of wood just a few inches away from my face. This was especially true as I got towards the deeper end where I could not possibly touch the bottom of the pool. It's amazing what the survival instinct can do for you. On the bright side, no one in my class drowned and about half of us did learn to swim. I even managed to swim along all four sides of the pool, which got me the ultimate prize of the 100-yard certificate, which I proudly still have.

After school that day, I was feeling a bit tired from the swim and so instead of playing outside I decided to look for Uncle. I had been thinking about how Uncle was only seven years older than me when he went off to war. It made me think about what he went through and how life was so different for him now in the swinging sixties. It didn't seem fair that he lost his childhood so quickly.

When I found Uncle, he was luckily in a chatty mood, with his pint of beer in hand as usual. I never saw him drink more than one pint, which he slowly sipped while he talked. I had just sat down when he said he had a little story to tell me about the letter 'V', which sounded a bit mysterious to me.

He told me he had just finished all of his military training at Shoeburyness and was about to leave the dock area when an officer approached him. He said to Uncle, 'You look like a bright lad,' which got Uncle's immediate attention as he had just undergone all of this specialised war training and was feeling very knowledgeable and pretty confident.

He was taken by the arm and guided into a wooden hut, which was just large enough to accommodate a small table and one chair. Uncle said how proud he was of his country whereupon the officer pushed a blue identity card in front of him and handed him a pen. He kept his hand partly over the card, so Uncle could not read all of it. He then asked him if he would like the letter 'V' for Victory marked on his identity card, for a little extra money. Uncle was eager to please and so immediately said, 'Yes'. Upon signing it, the officer loudly said, 'Next please,' and Uncle was pushed out of the office and back onto the docks.

When Uncle got his first weekly wage, he saw that he was being paid £4 pounds 4 shillings for basic pay, £2 pounds 6 shillings and 8 pence for 'War Risk' and £1 extra for the 'V' marked on his card.

You would assume that laying your life on the line every day would attract some government benefits but he still had to pay income tax, union dues, pension insurance, and unemployment insurance. He sent 2 pounds home each payday to help with his mum and dad's food and rent. I think that this really shows what type of young man he was, to give more than half of his net wages to his family in addition to laying his life on the line fighting for his country and yet to somehow maintain a positive view of people and life.

It wasn't until a whole year later that Uncle learned what that 'V' meant: By signing the document that day he had agreed to enlist on any 'unspecified war mission'. If there was a major war initiative then Uncle had just agreed to take part in it. He said it took him to the front line of one of the best-known events of the war, but for now that is all he would tell me as it was time for me to go back upstairs to Mum. Before I left, Uncle said with a smile on his face that he never again signed a form without reading every word first—especially the small print!

After listening to Uncle's story, I went upstairs and overheard Mum saying something about Lorraine's family being offered a new flat. I thought nothing more of it and went off to my bedroom to find something to read.

A few days later, I learned a bit more about the basement flat. As I've mentioned, it was where Lorraine lived with her mum and dad and Rex the dog. I could look out of our kitchen window and down into the pit, which was a walled area where Rex would run up and down. Lorraine was a nice girl in her teens who was always with the dog. The family had just apparently been offered a nice flat in a new building, which was a rare chance for them to get away from the damp, mouldy walls and rats of their own flat. If they turned down this opportunity it could be years before another one might be offered to them. The only problem with the new flat was that dogs were not allowed. They desperately wanted to move and so made the difficult decision of having their young healthy pet put down.

On the appointed day of Rex's demise, I was sitting on the front door step idly tossing a ball in the air; it felt as if I was waiting for a funeral procession to pass by. The basement door opened and then it closed briefly before opening again. Lorraine's mum came out followed by Lorraine, with Rex in tow on a lead. They all looked tired from lack of sleep and had a stoic look on their faces. Rex knew something was wrong and had his tail and head down. But this had to be done; what choice did they have?

They were climbing up the stairs to street level when Mum walked up to Lorraine's mum. They had a discussion for what seemed like ages but was probably about five minutes. I couldn't quite hear what they were saying and since it was always being made clear to me that 'children should be seen and not heard', I sat quietly on the step wondering why the funeral procession had been held up. After a few minutes, they went on their way, and Mum told me that Rex was being taken to the Blue Cross vets at Victoria. Lorraine had to kill the love of her 15-year-old life, the one love that had slept at the bottom of her bed every night and had kept her company in the dark, damp flat.

It was lunch time and I was just tucking into a cheese and pickle sandwich when Dad unexpectedly appeared in the kitchen. He usually worked through the day but he had a fare nearby and just decided to drop in. There were mutterings between Mum and Dad and then he quickly left in the cab. About an hour later, I was sitting on the front step when Dad reappeared in the cab. In the back I could see Lorraine and her mum.

Mum came down the steps and as the cab door opened, out jumped Rex! The two women talked for a few minutes, heads nodding in agreement, and then Mum walked over to me to announce that Rex would now be living with us! A life had been saved and I now had a dog to play with. Life was good…what an amazing day!

Lorraine brought Rex up to our living room a few times that week to get him used to our house, and by the weekend she and her family had gone and Rex had officially moved in with us.

After Lorraine's family moved out, there was an interesting turn of events. The next family to move into the basement flat had a lot of 'strange goings-on', according to Mum. They had a dubious income and the phrase 'a bit of a rogue' was used frequently in discussions to describe them. This was code for, there was something illegal about what they were doing, but it was always followed by 'if you ask me no questions, I will tell you no lies'.

Apparently, when the basement occupants were working on their next not exactly legal 'job' they would take orders from interested 'customers'. So, say that a customer wanted a cheap bottle of whiskey for an up-coming event, they would make sure that it was included in the shopping list for the next 'job'.

The going rate for these acquired objects was 50 percent of the cost on the legal open market. We apparently acquired many bargains in this manner, all paid for in untraceable cash.

I have no idea how much money this actually saved us or if Mum used their services often, because she loved to shop anyway, and that didn't slow down just because we could get 50 percent off on certain goods. And, of course, being just a child, it was none of my business.

CHAPTER 7

CHANGES

Easter was fast approaching and I was still pursuing my dream of a kiss from Anthony. There were a few moments where we had been together but it seemed we were always surrounded by a lot of people. I think it weighed on his mind too. Many times, we would be close and both would stop talking and look at each other out of the corner of our eyes. I thought it was up to him to make a move but I wanted to be close just in case. So I invited him to come to the judging of the daffodil competition since most of the boys didn't get involved with a girly thing like growing flowers. I thought if he saw me win, he would be overjoyed and be able to kiss me as part of the celebration.

I had a competitive streak in me, even in those days, and so I would look forward to the daffodil-growing competition. Early each year, the school would give every pupil a late-flowering daffodil bulb wrapped in a brown paper bag. Mum and I would plant the bulb in a pot and I would water it. This was serious stuff to a 10-year-old; I hated to fail at anything and so I checked on my plant each day. It was always a good sign when the green shoot started to peak through the soil. By the time the flower was in bud, I knew that the show was near.

A few days before the Easter holidays, we all brought our daffodils to school. The main hall was turned into a flower show for the day. All you could see was row, upon row, upon row of yellow bobbing daffodil heads. Wordsworth would have been proud; there were indeed 'a host of golden daffodils'.

The tallest daffodil would get first prize with second prize going to a less well cared for one. The judges would place a certificate by each plant, and every daffodil received an award for effort. Later in life these rudimentary gardening skills encouraged me to grow my own garden plants and vegetables. I was very happy to see that my daffodil had a 'First Place' certificate by its side! Everything was going according to plan.

When Anthony came into the hall, I couldn't wait for him to see my First Prize award. He walked towards my flower but then…disaster: Most of the other boys were huddled outside the hall as if stepping inside would be like walking into the girls' toilet. I had essentially invited Anthony into the girls' toilet without realising it. The boys made fun of him for coming into the hall, laughing and calling him names. So he left really quickly and without even looking in my direction. I was so worried that his humiliation meant that I would never see him again.

The Easter holidays had arrived and so I was tasked with accompanying Mum on one of her shopping trips. As I said, Mum's favourite thing to do was shop—for food and clothes and anything for the house. She justified this as honing another 'skill' required of the female gender.

You have to understand that shopping was very different in those days. To buy anything we had to walk to where it was sold and then try to work out how to physically get the larger and heavier items back to the house. We did much of our food shopping on the same day that the item was to be used.

Food shopping and food preparation were an almost constant daily process. There were very few convenience foods, no microwaves and very few frozen foods. We, along with most people, only owned a tiny freezer, which was about 3 inches wide and inside the top of the fridge compartment. Ice cream was bought at the local shop and eaten immediately, meats and fish were bought fresh and eaten that day or the next. Meats, after being cooked, were left on the countertop to cool down and were then covered over to keep the flies off—they were not put in the fridge. When we had sausages, Mum would leave them out at room temperature for several hours so that they could 'sweat' to bring out the full flavour of the meat. There was no thought given to the increase in bacterial count in the food, which could lead to food poisoning. Milk was poured in a jug and left out to be used throughout the day; eggs and all fruits and vegetables were also left on the countertop as were cheeses, which were never cooled. By today's standards it sounds unhygienic, but we were all heathy and had few problems with food poisoning.

As I have mentioned before, Mum was very clothes conscious and as a consequence of which, she always wore very fashion-forward clothes. She would dress up for any occasion, even when doing something as mundane as going blackberry picking. One of her favourite outfits was a navy-blue, polka-dot sun dress, complete with a wide, white, off-the-shoulder Marilyn collar and numerous puffy petticoats; the only acknowledgement that this was a casual event was the bandana headscarf, which was, of course, also in navy blue with white polka dots. As my brother and I were always trailing behind Mum when out shopping, we would often be witnesses to the challenge of her fashionable stiletto-heeled shoes. Stiletto heels were thin, 3-inch high heels that all the women of the day walked miles in. Goodness knows how.

Every so often Mum would get the narrowest part of the heel caught in the tramlines running down the middle of the road. More often than not, this happened on the zebra crossing with its flashing orange light called a Belisha beacon (named after a former minister of transport). Our little gaggle would stop mid-zebra with Mum hopping on one foot on her other 3-inch heel, as she deftly leant forward to wrestle the errant shoe from the clutches of the tramline. This happened so often that it was performed almost like a ballet, with her gracefully returning the unruly shoe to her nylon covered foot, and then quite suddenly we would be off again crossing the road and allowing the London traffic to continue on its way.

The very first American style shopping centre in Europe was just being built at the time on an old bomb site at the Elephant; when it was finished it would completely change how people shopped. This was in the days just before the first supermarkets, and shopping trolleys and the concept of placing the food in the trolley yourself did not exist. Certainly, women did not have a car to carry the shopping home in and very few women had a driving license. So the shopping venture was limited by how far you could walk and how much weight you could carry in the shopping bags. Shopping was quite a physical workout and took hours of your time.

Another place that we would shop at was East Lane Market. Sometimes we would get the number 12 bus and sometimes we would walk. The buses in those days were all red double-decker buses. My brother and I were experts at jumping on and off the open platform at the back of the bus and hanging on to the metal bars when the bus was moving.

East Lane was and still is a flourishing market. In those days, all of the stalls were owned by cockney Londoners, or costermongers. The air was thick with strong cockney accents, mostly men shouting their wares and quoting the bargain price for goods. Costermongers were sellers of fruits and vegetables and were a very close-knit community. Traditionally, costermongers would dress up on special occasions as Pearly Kings and Queens. They would wear clothes decorated with lots of mother-of-pearl buttons and parade the streets to raise money for charities.

My brother always joined us on trips to East Lane. The main focus for us on these outings was to make sure we did not lose sight of Mum in the crowds, as there were always lots of people at the market. When out shopping, Mum had an amazing ability to bob and weave through the crowds, just like Billy Walker the boxer. If we took our eyes off her for one second, she disappeared. On more than one occasion, my brother and I would be standing by ourselves, the crowds pushing around us, hoping that Mum would notice we were not with her. I can remember many a moment of panic thinking that she had gone and left us alone forever.

Mum would pick up fruit and vegetables and some tins of food at the market. There were also, however, a few treats for us; we would sometimes stop for some sarsaparilla from the 'Sarsaparilla man', whom everyone who went to the market knew. The drink was sweet, hot, and red-coloured and was very warming on a cool winter's day. Then there were the times we'd be treated to a bowl of jellied eels.

Eel (which was the only fish that could survive the polluted River Thames and, therefore, considered food for the poor) has a mild fishy flavour and the gelatin (jelly) came from the broth it was cooked in. They were always eaten chilled, doused in malt vinegar, and served in a paper bowl with a plastic spoon. This was pretty much the only take-away food available—there were no fast-food restaurants in those days. On special occasions, we would get some pie and mash, which was a real treat as we actually sat down at the marble-topped tables with their ornate cast-iron legs. The pie was filled with minced lamb and it was always accompanied with mashed potato and liquor (parsley sauce).

When we had finished shopping at the market we would go in through the back door of Marks & Spencer's on Walworth Road. In those days, all our clothing and, of course, their famous, almost indestructible underwear was bought at Marks'. As Mum was determined that we would never wear secondhand clothes, as she had had to suffer through, she would always buy new clothing almost weekly at this well-loved shop.

The next shopping trip was to David Greig's, the grocers. It was just me and Mum, as my brother was being looked after by Auntie. The reason for our trip was to get Black Forest ham on the bone, which apparently was the tastiest part of the animal and a highly praised delicacy.

David Greig's was an old-style Victorian shop with bright white- and blue-coloured mosaics on the walls and the floor. There was a long white marble counter behind which stood the assistants. The shop was always spotlessly clean and you had to ask the assistant to pass the food to you; even tins of food had to be requested and handed over the counter. It was a slow and leisurely pace of shopping, and there were always a lot of older ladies waiting in line in their dark coats and sensible flat leather shoes, their hair tightly pinned under hairnets. At the end of the store was a window where you paid the cashier for the goods. It took the whole morning to walk to the shop, wait in line, be served, and walk back to the house again. All that effort for Black Forest ham on the bone!

Another well-known shop at the Elephant was Bob White's, a local seafood shop. It had the best cockles and prawns, which were an essential ingredient for Sunday's seafood afternoon tea. Now to get to Bob White's we would have to walk through an area of prefabricated housing, which we called 'the prefabs'. After WWII ended, prefabricated temporary housing was erected on the old bomb site ruins to deal with the severe housing shortage. These were homes that were completely built at the factory and then installed at the site using a crane; all the builders then had to do was hook up the plumbing and electrical connections and they were ready for families to move in. They were quite nice inside and people had made an effort to cultivate their brand-new gardens. As with most temporary things, they were up for decades longer than was intended. Sir Michael Caine was raised in one of them.

Further along from the prefabs we passed Rowton House, built in 1897 by the Victorian philanthropist Lord Rowton to provide decent accommodation for working men. In the 1960s, it was known as a place where the 'tramps' and 'dossers' would go, who we would now call street people. It was a place that I was told to never go near by myself. It was instilled in me that it was a dangerous place as the people there were often alcoholics and had severe mental health problems, for which in the 1960s there was very little medical or social support.

Having negotiated the perils of Rowton House we would

eventually arrive at Bob White's and join the long line of women with their shopping bags, all queueing up for fresh seafood for Sunday tea. The produce was laid out on pristine white marble; the front of the store had a large glass window and the shop was filled with the smell of fresh fish. The seafood would be measured by the pint and placed in brown paper bags. In fact, all shopping was placed in paper bags; I don't remember any plastic bags used for food.

For Sunday tea, we all sat around the dining room table. It was always cockles, whelks, prawns, and jellied eels accompanied by Hovis brown bread and lots of butter. This was washed down with copious amounts of tea. Auntie and Uncle would join us together with any visiting aunts, uncles, or cousins. The house was always full of relatives of one kind or another, and they would bring with them the latest ups and downs of family life.

At this particular tea, I was chatting to my cousin and telling her about Mum's tearful eyes during the secret adult discussion and what Uncle Ern had said. Well, that was a mistake, as eagle-eared Mum heard me! I was vaguely aware of the chair scraping against the floor as Mum stood up. She then shouted at me to mind my own business and reminded me in no uncertain terms that children should be seen and not heard, and that I had no idea what I was talking about. The rest of the tea took place in stony silence, and other than me being asked to pass the plate of bread, not a single word was spoken by anyone. Everyone left the table as soon as they could, half of the food left uneaten, that was something else that had not happened before. Life was becoming more and more unpredictable and, well, I just didn't understand it.

In those days, most children were undernourished and really existed on the extra calories from sweets and treats. In our house, however, Mum believed that we should never be short of good-quality food and so would always cook us sumptuous meals with delicious 'afters', such as apple pie and custard, or steamed pudding and custard, or jelly and tinned fruit with Carnation milk. I think in part the emphasis on food stemmed from rationing during the war; after all, it was only 10 years earlier that rationing was still in place. When Mum grew up there was always a shortage of food—it had to be eked out. When the country was under siege, milk, eggs, butter, meat, and cheeses were among the basics in short supply. So needless to say, food was aplenty and as I mentioned earlier, I was carrying a few extra pounds. In those days, carrying a little extra weight was considered, well, at least in my family, a sign of good health. Being thin was a sign of illness.

Sadly, for me, Jean Shrimpton who was tall, thin, and waif-like was the model of choice in those days and Mary Quant was the trendiest designer around. Both of these icons broke the popular mould of the 1950s, which was curvy models and replaced the look with the slim, boyish figure my family considered to be a sign of malnourishment. If Jean Shrimpton had had my mother, she would never have been a supermodel.

Now clothes shopping in the 1960s was a completely different experience for me than for other thinner girls of my age and a real challenge. Accordingly, if you did not have the body of a supermodel, it was tough finding any clothes to fit. The only plus-size clothing was for matronly women in their fifties and over and the material bore the resemblance of heavy curtains. So if you were on the heavy side, it was a major multi-day event to find clothes that fitted and were trendy. It was also the days of communal changing rooms, with up to 20 other girls in one large room, all trying on clothes at once. I wanted to avoid these like the plague as the girls all seemed to be stick thin, except for me, but they were a necessary evil of clothes buying.

In those days, Carnaby Street was the fashion centre for the younger set. The new trend was trousers for teenage girls and women, and the 'A-line' was the dress shape of the moment. These were the days of white, spacey-looking clothing and this style was influenced by the space-race look—shiny, very square, and boxy—and it used new synthetic materials, such as Terylene and Lurex. Crimplene was another recently available fabric of choice as it did not require ironing, I noticed with some importance, as the age for me learning the 'skill' of ironing was fast approaching.

This was the first time that youth had their own designs and that young girls were no longer dressing as their mothers had dressed but defining a style of their own. But even in the early sixties, women were expected to wear dresses with stockings and hats. The 1960s is known as the era of the miniskirt, but back in 1963 hemlines were still modest and hovered around the knees. Fashions and stereotypes were changing but very slowly.

Mum and I would spend hours trying on dresses. That is if Mum did not do one of her disappearing acts. To me, then, clothes shopping was a stressful mix of squeezing into clothes paired with the embarrassment of communal changing rooms and the constant fear of being abandoned by Mum. This, sadly, would not be my last time and was destined to be a repeating nightmare in my 10-year-old life.

Talking of nightmares, I was longing to know what was worrying the adults as they were all doom and gloom yet again. It was turning out to be just one disaster after another, and then Mum finally told me the bad news: The printing factory was definitely closing. The place that gave work to almost all of our family was shutting down and moving to Bracknell in a county called Berkshire, a place that none of us had ever heard of.

I was told that lots of new homes were being built in this new place called Bracknell and that there were large tax incentives for businesses to move there. The factory owner had been offered a brand-new building, which was warm and dry and much cheaper to heat and run. The ladies were thrilled to hear that it had indoor toilets.

Following negotiations and concerns of the Lamlash families, all workers would be provided with a new home, new school places for their children, and better living conditions. For them, it was a deal too good to be true, but it also meant that most of the family would be moving away.

I then learned something terrible: We could not move with them. Dad was licensed as a London taxi driver and so we had to stay in London. We would not have been offered a new home as Dad did not work for the factory, and if we moved to Bracknell, Dad would have had no work. Soon we would have to go our separate ways; my cousins and all my uncles and aunts would move away without us. I felt so lost and so sad.

But I suppose at least Easter was only a few days away and I could look forward to eating my chocolate Easter eggs, which were always lined up on the top of the piano. Some years, I had as many as five chocolate eggs, all of which had their pride of place. I knew exactly what to expect on Easter Sunday, except that wasn't quite what happened. As I mentioned earlier, I had told Mum I didn't want to learn the piano anymore and since then the piano had just gathered dust in the living room.

Well, on Good Friday, the piano was unexpectedly moved by Dad but without Mum's sanction…I heard the sound of sawing in the vicinity of the flat roof, and as I peeked through the doggie flap, I saw Dad sawing my piano into pieces! Eventually, all that was left was a pile of wood and piano wires. When Mum saw this, she went white with anger and told me to play outside. As I left, I could hear her shouting at Dad. This meant that my Easter eggs were relegated to the coffee table! Could nothing stay the same as it used to be?

Easter came and went, not quite as I expected, but anyhow I was soon back at school and focusing on my plan. The end of the school year was weeks away but I felt as though I was running out of time to kiss Anthony. He had only been a bit odd towards me for a few days after the daffodil embarrassment. There would be several chances at the end of the year for us to be alone, such as parties to celebrate another successful school year and with them an opportunity for that kiss. Anthony did ask his mum if I could come over to play at their house but she seemed to think that was inappropriate. I couldn't even think of asking Mum to let Anthony play at our house. So still no kiss!

CHAPTER 8

THE UNEXPECTED

I was just getting ready to leave for school one morning and was trying to decide between the sinister Jack the Ripper Fives Court route to school or the long route along St. Georges Road, when Mum said she would pick me up from school at 11 o'clock because I had an appointment with the doctor.

Well, this was news to me but at least I got to leave school early, which was always a bonus. At the appointed time, I was released from class and met Mum at the front gate. We got on the double-decker bus to Great Ormond Street Children's Hospital. Great Ormond Street is yet another Victorian-built building, but it was also so much more than this thanks to the interests of Roald Dahl (the beloved children's book author) and J. M. Barrie (who left the rights and income from his story *Peter Pan* to the hospital). It is a hospital of high expertise. In 1962, the hospital developed the first heart and lung bypass machine for children. Over the years, they have also been at the forefront of UK clinical trials for children.

So that morning I walked into the very capable hands of this institution. Mum and I sat in the large waiting room on brown cloth-covered chairs. I spent my time swinging my legs while looking at the painted institutional walls of bottle green and cream. My name was called and off we trotted to the doctor. Mum spoke to him, and towards the end of the conversation, the doctor actually spoke to me, which was highly unusual in those days. I apparently needed to have my tonsils removed to stop the coughs and colds I was always succumbing to. This would require a stay in the hospital and some kind of operation. It would also involve a few weeks off school—always good——and jelly and ice cream during the recovery period. This all seemed to me to be quite a good deal.

Mum didn't want to wait until summer for the operation and have it delay our holiday plans. My school marks were very good and she had already cleared it with the teacher. I would go into the hospital in a couple of days.

Then it hit me like a lead balloon: I would miss all the end of year parties and my chance to kiss Anthony! I was so upset. Just moments before I had been so happy about all the ice cream I was going to get, but now a stay in the hospital seemed like the worst plan that had ever been hatched.

On the appointed day, I went to the hospital again with Mum. I got undressed and hopped into my bed on the ward. Mum made sure I had everything that I needed and then went home to my brother and left me in the care of the nurses. There were 10 other children in the ward, their beds arranged in a horseshoe shape about the room. The ceilings were 10 feet high and covered in plaster coving, all painted white; I spent a lot of time lying in bed and looking at that ceiling during my time there.

In the middle of the floor was an activity table where we could play with toys and eat our meals. This was my first day and none of us were being fed very much, just some sweet drinks. Mum came to visit me in the late afternoon and sat in a chair at the end of the bed, chatting about nothing in particular. She came every day that I was in the hospital and brought me some jigsaw puzzles and colouring books to help pass the time.

We were told that we were all in for the same reason and that we would all have our surgery on the same day but at different times. The next day, one by one, we were given something to make us drowsy before we went into the operating room. I remember falling asleep in the ward and then later, waking up in the ward with a sore throat. As the doctor had promised, we had jelly and ice cream as our main meal that day; this had never happened before and life felt pretty good.

Mum arrived later with a little surprise. Mr. Chapel had told the whole class to make Get Well cards for me so Mum had brought with her 40 handmade and personally coloured-in cards from each of my classmates. They were all signed, some with nice messages, and others with just pictures and a signature. Mr. Chapel may have been a fearful man but he also had his soft side. I still have the cards to this very day.

I was discharged from the hospital a few days later but was told not to go back to school for a fortnight so that I might rest. Mum and I fought several times as I said that I was feeling fine and more than ready to return to school. She couldn't understand why I was so desperate to get back, our roles had completely reversed! But then, how could she know that the weeks were slipping by and I was desperate in my need for a kiss from Anthony. Was love changing me? The reality is that love changes us all, even if you're only 10.

While I was increasingly impatient at being forced to rest at home, Uncle popped up to see me and asked how I was feeling and if I needed anything. I told him that I had really enjoyed listening to his last story and I wondered if he had any others as it would really help to take my mind off of my sore throat. Uncle, being the caring person that he was, happily obliged.

He told me that before he had signed up for service, he worked at the Rubber Stamp Company in the City of London, preparing stamps for use with the ration books.

He said that when he turned 17, he received a letter to say that he was enlisted to join the war effort; he was called to serve in the RAF as an air gunner and duly reported to Hendon Aerodrome to be assessed. Now to serve as an air gunner you had to pass a maths test, which 'luckily' Uncle failed. He joked that failing the maths test probably saved his life, as a high percentage of the gunners were killed in battle.

As Uncle had escaped the fate of an air gunner, he was then offered other options for service. His next option was to join the tank corps; the tanks were noisy and claustrophobic and as his brother was in the tank corps he had a pretty good idea of the difficult conditions. He immediately turned that opportunity down.

Uncle's options then narrowed to either the Bevin Boys or the Merchant Navy. The Bevin Boys were coal miners and were named after a trade union official and Labour Party politician, Ernest Bevin. Britain at that time was desperate for miners to provide fuel for the war factories and to keep people's homes warm, and so conscription into the coal mines began. Mining working conditions were very dangerous and so Uncle decided to apply for his last option, which was as a trimmer with the Merchant Navy. Now Uncle was not quite sure what a trimmer was but he was hoping that it was a safer option than air gunner, tank corps, or coal mining, and as this was his final option, he took a chance and said he would sign up. He added that he may have been patriotic but that didn't mean he had left his will to live behind; and besides, he added with that twinkle in his eye, he had just started to court a rather fetching lady named Ellen (known to me as Auntie). Little did Uncle know then where his choice would take him.

Talking of the unknown, Dad often came home with stories about picking up interesting fares in the cab. I don't know if Mum was trying to make me feel better but she popped into my bedroom and told me about an American family that Dad picked up. They were the Kroh family from Los Angeles, which she told me was in California in the United States. It was apparently the same place where all of the Hollywood films were made. Dad had taken the family on a tour of the London sights, and Mum had written to them a few times. They gave me a one dollar bill, which I found fascinating and still have to this day. Years later, I got to visit Hollywood and thought of the Kroh family and that one dollar.

Mum also had a second story to tell me as well. She said that the very same week that Dad picked up the Krohs, he had picked up Tommy Steele, who she said was a very big star. His family lived in the same neighbourhood as us and so Mum felt that he was extra special. She also said that he had given Dad a good tip, so not only was he a local boy made good but also someone who shared his good fortune. In Mum's eyes, Dad could not get a better passenger.

I was starting to feel a bit better after my operation and after the couple of weeks had passed, I was allowed back at school. I carried on as usual, seeing my friends and riding my bike at the bomb site. Me and the gang had a lot of fun and giggled like crazy, and there were many times when I wanted the kiss with Anthony to happen but there were always just too many other kids around that stopped it from happening. I even hoped that someone would dare us, like before, but for some reason no one ever did again. Maybe because they knew that we were dying to kiss and it was, therefore, not much of a dare. I was getting desperate. I decided I would just kiss him and get it over with. I didn't care where. But there was only one week to go before the end of the term, and as much as I tried to get that kiss, it seemed that we were never alone for long enough. School finished all too soon, and I realised that I would just have to put the kiss on hold until after the summer break.

Now it was time to enjoy our family summer holiday. Mum said that although money had to be earned to keep food on the table, holidays were also very important. We would always have two weeks away from London. One year we rented a caravan on Canvey Island in Essex. It was a lot of fun except that there was only one communal toilet block, which was a five-minute walk away. Trekking out to it after dark in my nightdress, walking across the muddy field holding a torch, and going into the dark, insect-filled toilet was a terrifying ordeal. Fortunately, Mum decided that not having an indoor toilet was below the standards for our family and so our future holidays all had indoor toilets.

Sure enough, this year we were at a Pontins holiday camp, with an indoor bathroom and toilet. It had the added bonus of being fully catered, as Mum had also announced it was not a holiday for her if she was still cooking for everyone.

Most of the holiday camps at Pontins were left over buildings from WWII. Some had housed prisoners of war or soldiers and they often had a lot of land surrounding them. So after the war effort had wound down, some were converted into what we would now call resorts. On day one of the holiday we would pack up Dad's taxi with lots of blankets and pillows and drive off at the crack of dawn to our destination. It was a long drive of about four or five hours and at some stage either I or my brother would feel car sick so we would have to make a few stops along the way.

This year we stayed in a chalet, which was really an open-plan room with two bunk beds and a double bed for the parents. The chalets were mostly in single-story buildings. Pontins, like Warners, was a five-star holiday camp. We only once stayed at Butlins when we met up with some family members who were staying there. Butlins was quite cramped and there were a lot more people around all the time. But the camp that Mum chose for us had more space and better entertainers and things to do. At Pontins, the entertainment staff were called Blue Coats and there was a full day and evening children's entertainment programme. This was bliss! It meant I could be independent from Mum and Dad. Any spare time I had I would spend in the swimming pool. What I liked about the holiday was the freedom. We only had one rule: That we should not go off the campsite. Other than that, I was free to do what I wanted. Mum and Dad were in holiday mode but always around somewhere; or if something happened, I could grab a Blue Coat and they would send out an announcement for my parents over the Tannoy speaker system.

We had three meals a day in the main dining room, which were served to us at the table. I still remember the distinctive smell of the breakfast cereal and the milk first thing in the morning, odd thing to remember that. Our table was for the four of us and was always laid out with knives, forks, and plates and we had ladies serving our food to us, which for a

10-year-old was quite a special thing. After dinner, we would get changed and go off to the main entertainment for the evening. There would be early shows for children, like magic shows. Once I was chosen to go up to the magician and be his assistant. The trick involved a silver box and I had to say that there was nothing in it, which there wasn't, but then the magician suddenly produced some playing cards from it. I still don't know how he did it. I do know that after that holiday I had a fascination about how magic tricks worked. I got magic sets of my own for Christmas and spent hours reading them and practising the tricks.

We came home from holiday and the rest of the summer passed without incident. I played in the street with Susan and most afternoons I went to the Tabernacle for the children's summer Bible camp. I did crafts and listened to stories from the New Testament. After the unexpected end of the school year, the summer itself was fairly predictable. I started thinking that maybe my life was beginning to improve!

CHAPTER 9

MY NIGHTMARE

Over the summer our gang didn't really meet up. We tended to spend more time with cousins so I didn't really see much of Anthony. But that is the way it always was. So with September just around the corner, I was really looking forward to seeing him again, exchanging those paper notes with the 'x's' between us, and getting that long-awaited kiss that had been postponed the *whole* of the summer.

On the first day back at school, I eagerly looked out for him. But he wasn't there. Was he ill or something? He wasn't there the next day either. Maybe he would be at school on Monday? But by Monday of the second week of school, I knew something was very wrong as his name wasn't on the school register. Then I heard the terrible news: his family had moved away!

Just when I thought that my life was beginning to improve, my Anthony, the love of my life, was gone, just like that. I suddenly felt so alone and so very, very sad. I would never touch that warm hand again or look into those eyes; I would never have that gentle first kiss. We would never sit next to one another and talk about everything and nothing, which was the most fascinating thing in the world. There would be no more notes and no more little 'x's'. I was devastated. This was the worst thing that had ever happened to me in my long 10-year-old life!

I told Mum and Auntie when I got back from school and then spent the rest of the day in my room. Nobody bothered me. It was washing day and after school I would usually help with bringing in the washing from the line but Mum asked my brother to help her out instead. I just sat on my bed unable to believe that my future did not have Anthony in it. I did not even know where he had moved to. I had no address or even a telephone number. I was just a child and children were not consulted in such adult matters as moving house. All I could do was stare at my bedroom wall until eventually Mum called me for dinner. I picked at the food on the plate and then got ready for bed. I was relieved when I finally got to sleep that night and could escape the horrible reality of my world.

As October approached and my eleventh birthday loomed on the horizon, I thought still of my lost love. I had a lot of time to think about him and what we had done together. Here I was, almost a teenager, feeling all grown up and yet all alone without him in my life. I don't know if Mum could see my sadness or if she was still in busy mode because of the factory closing, but she had decided that this would be the year for a blow-out birthday for me.

The word went out that I was going to have a birthday party. We lived in a close-knit community of friends who went to the same school, who played together, and went to one another's parties. At school, there were usually 40 children in a classroom, which was really designed for only 30; this over-population was mostly as a result of the baby-boom after the war. Birthday parties, therefore, were always very large.

The downside of this population boom for women was that they were seen solely as mothers and wives, it was very rare for a woman to have her own source of income. Women were financially dependent upon their husbands and also had their future career options and independence severely limited. But then the war had been all about personal sacrifice by the individual for the benefit of the country as a whole; this was just a continuation of getting the country back on its feet. The country needed to increase the population and the returning male war heroes needed work. So women were persuaded to leave paid work and return to the home to raise a family and provide a peaceful and tranquil home for their husbands.

In preparation for my party, Mum asked what games I wanted to play. As it seemed as if I could ask for anything, I asked for all my favourites: Musical Chairs, Pass the Parcel and Pin the Tail on the Donkey. The next thing to be decided was Mum's favourite topic—what would I wear! I was duly dragged back to the shops and returned to the ongoing torture of trying to find a dress that fit me, all the while trying on said item in a fitting room full of stick-thin girls. Mercifully, this time we found a dress in half a day, at C&A's. It was a navy blue 'twist dress'. I liked it because it had a pleated skirt so that when I danced, especially to Chubby Checker's *Let's Twist Again*, it would spin out. I felt pretty in the dress but trendy at the same time; these were very important things for an almost 11-year-old!

On the appointed day, the living room furniture was arranged in readiness for the party. The chairs were placed around the walls, the dining table was covered in a paper table-cloth, sandwiches and cakes were laid out, ready to be eaten. Everything was ready and there I sat in my new twist dress waiting for my friends to arrive. After what seemed like forever, the doorbell rang. It was Jeannie Skinner, a school friend. She looked smart and all dressed up for my party. Before long, all my other friends and family arrived too. Now it was a party!

The party started off with Musical Chairs. We walked around the chairs, which had been set out in the middle of the room to music but there was always one less chair than the number of people circling them. When the music stopped, we pushed one another out of the way to sit on a chair. Two people on one chair was not allowed, and the adult in charge would referee who should leave the game. The last one to oc-cupy the one remaining chair got the prize.

The next game was Pin the Tail on the Donkey, in which you would be blindfolded and have to pin a paper tail on the hand-drawn picture of a donkey. The person who got the tail nearest the donkey's bottom won.

The last party game was Pass the Parcel. A mystery parcel would have multiple layers of wrapping paper on it. While the music played, we would pass the parcel from one person to the next. When the music stopped, the person holding the parcel would tear off as many layers as possible but it had to be one layer at a time and only until the music started again. The game finished when the parcel was fully unwrapped and the person holding it then got to keep the gift!

After the games finished, Mum proudly brought out the homemade birthday cake. It had peach-coloured buttercream icing, which was so expertly done that you would have thought we had our own private chef! It was very tasty as well.

Everything was homemade. This was partly because everyone was living on very small budgets, with just one income per family. It was also because it was the assigned role of the housewife to provide expert-level food for the family. Parties were always full of fun and laughter and we were constantly running around giggling. There was no such thing as a catered party at McDonald's, but we always had lots of homemade sandwiches, cake, and fizzy drinks and had a great time!

At the party, everyone was happy. We ate our fill, then everyone sang 'Happy Birthday' and I blew out the candles on the cake. Then it was present time, time to unwrap the gifts that the guests had brought, and I was delighted with them. I got little boxes of chocolates from most people, except for Jeannie Skinner who got me a box of fancy hankies.

The party was a huge success! Everyone had a great time, even the parents who hovered at the edges of the party were laughing and joking. There was not one electronic beep—not like children's parties nowadays. But for me there was just one thing missing and that was my Anthony. If only he had been there to see me in my twist dress, it would have been perfect.

Speaking of electronic beeps, 1963 was also the year when science and technology for kids arrived on TV in the form of the BBC's *Doctor Who*. This was the new science program for children, which included scientific theories, such as Einstein's Theory of Relativity and the basic physics of time all wrapped up in the form of a tale about a fictitious doctor and space monsters. It also explored some historical plot lines about the past and how things might be in the future. I absolutely loved the show because the girls were independently minded and curious, like me. No one was wearing frilly dresses and there was not one poodle in sight! I have been a fan of *Doctor Who* ever since then.

We had actually arrived in the age of science and technology in 1962, with the launch into space of the first Telstar satellite. This was followed by Telstar 2 in 1963. The significance of these satellites was that for the very first time in history, television and telephone calls could be communicated live across the Atlantic Ocean between the UK and North America. Such things were still out of reach for the ordinary person but they were possible—very different from today with its free video calls via Skype.

There was also a song in the 'Top 10' music charts that celebrated this new space age. I was so proud to have the song in my very small but modern 45 rpm record collection. It was called *Telstar* by the pop group the Tornadoes. I was surrounded, at the tender age of 11, by the concept that we could do anything with science and technology and that even going to the moon was possible!

After the party had finished and all my friends had gone home, I popped down to see Uncle. He asked if I had enjoyed my party and said how nice my birthday cake looked. He then told me that during the war he had been a judge in a cake-baking competition in New York. Of course, this immediately appealed to my sense of adventure and interest in travel and so I asked him to tell me more.

He said that after his leave from the Merchant Navy was over, he was transferred to another ship, again working in the boiler room. This time he was in a convoy traveling across the Atlantic Ocean to North America. Before leaving England, he had tried to let his family know where he was going to be traveling to next. All letters home were read and censored before being sent so as not to give away the positions of any ships to the enemy. If you wanted to say that you were in the United States then you referred to 'visiting your Uncle Sam' and if you wanted to let your family know that you were on the way back to England then you would write about chalk (this referred to the chalky-white cliffs of the Dover coastline).

Uncle then pulled out a small grey piece of paper from

his pocket and handed me his Port of New York Coastguard Pass, which had his thumbprint on it for identification. It was issued on the 1st of April 1944 when he was just 18.

While in port, his ship was loaded with food and munitions for the return trip across the Atlantic. Britain, being an island, required more than a million tons of imported material each week to provide just the basic provisions to its population and the war effort. At that time in Britain rationing was in place for food and clothing; people were also growing their own food and the role of the women was to 'stretch' food to keep families fed. Uncle told me that the Americans looked upon them as poor relatives; several of the New York ladies' clubs gave out cardigans, gloves, and balaclavas to him and his shipmates; all with a little note saying, 'I knitted this article with love to keep you warm at sea.' The women wanted to know how bad it really was back in England. He said they were treated like visiting heroes and told how brave they were to stand up to the Germans.

While in port, Uncle and 12 of the crew were invited to a New York ladies' club to judge a cake competition. Twenty elderly ladies had made cakes with various jams and creams. Uncle and his crew were to be the judges. Now Uncle had not cooked a thing in his whole life and so wondered how on earth he was going to judge the best cake! All the boys were about 18 years of age and at home their mothers would always have cooked for them. But they went ahead and tasted the cakes, formed a huddle to talk about the results, and all agreed that the oldest lady at 73 years of age would get their vote. He told me that, much to their relief, all the lady club members agreed. With that, Uncle and his friends bid their goodbyes and went off to explore the city of New York, their brief encounter with baking competitions now over.

The next day, his ship was being readied for the return trip to Portsmouth in Britain. During the loading process, the ship's fireman fell on the gangway and was taken to the hospital. Uncle was swiftly promoted from trimmer to fireman, which he was very pleased about. As a trimmer, his main job was to move the coal around in the bunker so that the ship would not list to one side in the water. However, a fireman quite literally tends the fire on the ship to keep the boiler working at full steam. Not only was Uncle happy because of the change of job but a fireman was paid more as well.

After the ship was loaded, it was moved into position to form part of the convoy for the return trip. The ships traveled in groups, which made it easier to provide air and sea cover to protect the important goods that they were carrying from being sunk at sea. The ship convoy traveled with the naval escorts spaced between each of the Merchant Navy vessels. Tragically, on this trip back to Britain, the convoy was attacked and there were lost ships—and lost lives.

What he did not tell me until many years later was that the image of losing fellow mariners at sea never left him. He said that in the event the ships were hit, they were under strict orders not to stop to pick up any of the survivors. They could clearly see the men bobbing about in the cold Atlantic Ocean and all Uncle could do was watch them in the oily blackness, waiting for their death. Nets were placed over the side of the escort ships and if the shell-shocked men in the water had the ability to grab the nets then just a few might be saved. He said the real heroes during the war were the ones who didn't come back. All he could do was pray for them. In the Battle of the Atlantic, as it was called, 3,500 Merchant Navy ships were lost.

So it was with great relief that Uncle's ship finally reached Britain and as they anchored off Portsmouth Harbour, waiting their turn to go alongside and be unloaded, he sat on deck smoking a cigarette and counting his blessings, the first one of which was that he was still alive.

It so happened that a month after my birthday—the 5th of November—was another one of my favourite events. It was Guy Fawkes' Night, also known as Bonfire Night or Firework Night. There were two flat roofs on the house at 11b, one at the very top for the washing line and one over the kitchen, which was much smaller and had some flower boxes and a place for Rex to use. We had a doggy flap made in the door so that Rex could get in and out and onto the roof as needed.

The best use of the roof, though, was on Guy Fawkes' Night. Guy Fawkes was part of the group of traitors who tried to blow up the Houses of Parliament and assassinate King James I in 1605. The plot was foiled at the last minute and so to celebrate the king surviving the assassination attempt, we would set off fireworks from our little flat roof.

The firework night planning started a week earlier, with discussions about what type of fireworks to have and we would then go out to buy them. Brock's and Pains were the main firework manufacturers. My brother and I would look at them all behind a large glass screen and choose our favourite ones. I chose Catherine Wheels and Rockets, and we would buy enough sparklers for all the kids to hold and wave about in the dark. There would usually be about half a dozen people on the roof with us. It was a fun and exciting night as the other families in the neighbourhood would also be out in their gardens and on their roofs. We could look at the other houses and see all of the fireworks from the whole neighbourhood being set off at the same time. It was a night full of the sound of bangs, and coloured fireworks that lit up the night sky. The evening was always topped off with a special menu of jacket (baked) potatoes and baked sausages, which we were allowed to eat late in the evening.

It was a great night, but the next day we were back to the new reality of my life. People were starting to disappear from Lamlash to this place miles away from London in Berkshire. This continued throughout the autumn term and one by one classmates just stopped showing up at school. It turned out that the factory's move and approval to relocate the workers from Lamlash had been approved long before anyone had ever entered into negotiations. So all the drama and anger were for naught. It was a forgone conclusion but no one had any idea at the time.

There were only four of us in my gang now, which didn't

quite work with one boy and three girls. It was also a constant reminder of Anthony, who was missing. Unlike today where you might still remain friends, be on Facebook, or text now and again, back then all contact was lost when someone moved away.

I really didn't understand life; I had thought I knew exactly what it was all about but nothing made sense any more. I went to Uncle and told him that my world was falling apart and asked if things could get any worse. He could have made light of the situation as I was 'only a child', but no, he spoke of how young people often had to face difficult situations. I could see from the sadness in his eyes how his mind had gone back to the war days. Then he talked about something that, until now, he hadn't ever mentioned. It was quite a story.

Uncle said he had taken some leave after the Atlantic crossing and was just back on board his ship when they received notice to await a Royal Navy barge. After several hours, the barge came alongside and up the gangway came naval officers who were taken to the captain's quarters. Then over the loud speaker came the announcement: 'This is the captain speaking. Will all those crew with a "V" stamped on their identity card report to the saloon.'

Uncle and his mates all stared at each other and then looked at their cards and it was then as Uncle said, 'The penny dropped'. He remembered the officer on the dock who asked him if he wanted 'V' for victory on his identity card; he remembered signing a document…well, this was why he had been paid that extra money.

The Royal Navy captain addressed those men with the 'V' on their ID cards. He began by saying what a pleasure it had been sailing with them and that he hoped they would meet up again someday. They were then told to pick up their gear and to follow the naval officers and board the barge. Uncle still did not know what was happening but did notice that some of the crew were wearing Middle Eastern desert gear and so rumours started to fly that they were off to raid Rommel's headquarters in the Middle East (which was a hotly contested war area surrounding the Persian Gulf). Later they found out that the desert gear was just a ruse to confuse the German spies in England.

Uncle and his shipmates did as they were ordered and boarded the barge. They had no idea where they were being taken. In the distance, they could see a mass of troops and lorries, with huge warehouses in the background. They approached the shore and being British, the sailors were taken to one of the largest warehouses on the dockside and given a good strong cup of tea. They were then split up and assigned to ships to build up a full complement, the previous crew members having died at sea.

Uncle eventually learned that he was to be part of the D-Day landings, the Allied invasion of Normandy in June 1944, it was the largest seaborne invasion in history. He made several runs across and said that he could see that there were vast numbers of aircraft and ships. Deep-sea tugs towed the fuel pipeline from England; this was known as PLUTO (pipe-line under the ocean). He was in the second wave.

His ship towed part of the Mulberry Harbour, which was a temporary harbour set up at Arromanches Normandy, it was built to help with the rapid offloading of cargo. It was later named Port Winston after the wartime leader Winston Churchill. When Uncle's ship reached the harbour, there was active fighting, which meant that both the rear gun on his ship and the Lewis gun at midship were firing. To me it was a story you would see in a film at the cinema. Uncle was a hero; he was in amongst all the front-line fighting and gunfire. He was under direct fire from the enemy and in real danger of being killed.

In his convoy were British, Polish, and Czech troops. On his second run, the ship's rope nets were deployed and the landing craft came along side; as the troops started climbing down into the landing craft, they pushed money and letters into the hands of Uncle and the crew. Uncle said to one man, 'What makes you think that we will survive?' The trooper said, 'We are going into battle, you aren't, so you have a better chance than us.'

Uncle said to me that he wondered how many of those troops came back alive. There was one special person that did come back, however, and that was Uncle's brother. He had apparently been on the ship without Uncle knowing and had been deployed onto a landing craft.

His ship made a couple more trips to Caen after that, as part of the planned liberation of that town. He said that the civilians who lived there had put up with day and night bombing, with no way of defending themselves, other than with 'faith and prayer'.

Uncle's final word on this chapter in his life was that both he and his brother lost a good many friends because of the war, and that he was grateful that they both made it back alive. But he also said that 'the real heroes were the ones that did not come back,' and then, with real feeling, he added 'God rest their souls.'

After that conversation, I never really thought of Uncle in the same way again. Thereafter, I saw him as that quiet, unsung war hero, who had somehow, throughout all of the horror, stayed true to himself. He was still that slightly shy but chatty man with a twinkle in his eye, and he was one of the nicest and friendliest men that I have ever met.

CHAPTER 10

THE END OR THE BEGINNING?

And so here we are at the end of 1963 in what has been a year of change, a year that we all struggled with. I had thought that I knew it all, after all, I now had 11 years of experience to draw on. In my 'old' life it was clear who did what and what I was expected to do. At the beginning of the year, I had known everything, and by the end of the year, I felt as though I knew nothing at all. I found the love of my life and lost him. I thought my family would be with me forever and it turned out I was losing them as well. Although in true family tradition, everyone was struggling with change and trying at the same time to remain positive. We were trying to be strong despite knowing that things were never going to be quite the same again.

Thankfully, Christmas was fast approaching and for me it was and still is one of the most exciting days of the year. I was probably the only one in my class who said that she still believed in Father Christmas, but it seemed to me that I had a pretty good arrangement. I could ask 'Father Christmas' for the toys that I wanted and Mum and Dad (as his helpers) enjoyed providing them. I decided to let the fantasy continue for at least one more year…

Mum tried her best to make it a great family Christmas, but with everything that had happened that year—the secret family meetings, the raised voices, and the factory closing—Christmas had a dark pall over it.

Knowing that it was our last Christmas together as a family made it more intense than ever. My cousins were moving and so were my aunts and uncles. The people I had known all of my life were leaving. As an 11-year-old, I had no access to the telephone and once my family and friends were gone, I would never hear from them again. Children had limited rights and you just did what adults told you to do. There was little awareness of how children were feeling about these changes, as it was considered purely an adult matter. As long as we were fed and clothed and went to school, then all of our needs were being met. There was no understanding of our sense of loss or how losing our cousins and aunts and uncles was affecting us. Who would I go to when Mum was having a funny turn? Who would I talk to when something happened in my life that I did not understand? I had lost Anthony and now I was losing my family as well. I felt all alone.

With all the adults muttering about true grit and determination to get us through this 'happy season', come hell or high water, and with Mum having made up her mind that we were all going to be cheerful no matter what, it was a waste of effort to go against the tide. So we all just did whatever we were told to do and ran with the pack.

Mum was going to try to make this the best Christmas of all. She threw herself into preparations like never before. If this was going to be the year when the family were to be broken up, then she was determined that if we were not going to go out 'with a bang,' we were certainly not going to be going out with 'a whimper' …(to misquote T.S. Eliot).

Now obviously we did not have any extra money for this amazing Christmas. Dad was already working 12 hours a day as a cabbie and we never saw him, so money matters would have to be handled like a true professional. The first thing to go was the little Kensitas cigarette machine. My parents realised that they were smoking too much and it was costing them a small fortune. The idea that it was bad for their health was never a consideration. The little furniture-matching machine made its last clunk and was gone forever, and I became the cigarette runner once again.

The next item in this efficiency drive was that Mum announced we were going to make our own party clothes for Christmas Day. She bought a dressmaking pattern of two identical suits, one for me and one for her. It was a Chanel-styled suit with a straight skirt and a round-necked short jacket. Mum had some gorgeous blue slub material and mine was brown. We cut the dressmaking material on the (expensive) Beautility dining room table, which had a fold-down leaf. It had a rubber mat on it to protect the expensive teak wood (nothing but the best for us). We worked together reading the pattern instructions and sewing up the suit on the electric sewing machine. Mum's specialty was 'setting-in' the sleeves and mine was sewing in the zips. We were making our own clothes because money was tight, but I enjoyed dressmaking with Mum and I was so proud of my suit when it was finished. It was so much better than just buying one. It was also a huge relief that I did not have to endure the torture of the communal changing rooms for trying on clothes!

Attention now turned to party supplies, which had to be 'ordered' from the 'ask-me-no-questions' basement-dwellers. Whiskey and gin were ordered at a very 'competitive' price. Beer we would get elsewhere and was always a dark ale. Lemonade, as in previous years, was provided for us kids.

In those days, there was no sign of Christmas until a week before the event. The tree, a poor malnourished and deformed pine tree from the corner shop, was erected with pride in a plastic bucket filled with soil from the window box on the small flat roof. Each year we got out the same decorations and set of Christmas lights.

We used to call the lights 'union' lights. If one light went out, they all went out (very much like the trade unions of the day). And so every year we would all take it in turn to find out which light bulb was loose this time. It became a tradition to tighten the small light bulbs on the tree one by one while at the same time watching whatever was on the black and white

TV. Whoever was the light-checker would idly turn the lights, and when they eventually lit, there would be a chorus from everyone in the living room…they're on!

With the tree lit and the tinsel draped over its branches, it was time to put the gifts for the adults under the tree. There were no gifts for the children because Father Christmas was in charge of bringing those.

As we approached Christmas, everything was cleaned, scrubbed, and sparkling and so by the time we got to Christmas Eve, 'not a creature was stirring, not even a mouse'. This was because the creatures were exhausted from all the work and the mice had long since left 11b to find crumbs of food elsewhere.

At least this year, Christmas was still going to follow its predictable order of the day. I would begin the day by waking up and feeling the weight of the presents on the bottom of my bed, and the day would finish with the usual Christmas party. But in the previous year there had been at least a hundred of us at the party; this year there would be perhaps only 25 or 30. We all carried on as if this wasn't a problem but you could feel the emptiness even before the day started.

So as usual, in the early hours of Christmas Day, Father Christmas' four little helpers (Mum, Dad, Auntie, and Uncle), climbed the stairs to our bedrooms with a sack of toys, as they always had done. When I awoke, a big sack of presents had appeared on the bottom of my bed. I would always know that Father Christmas had visited because I felt the weight of the toys on my feet. But we were under strict instructions not to open them until it had started to get light outside. We were told that Father Christmas would know if we cheated and opened them early. Even though I only half believed in him, it seemed to me that there was no harm in hedging my bets by complying with this rule. So I lay in bed half asleep looking out the window for a sign of dawn.

Then at the first glimmer of light, I dragged the big sack off my feet and up to the top of the bed and began to delve into it. I looked out for the chocolates first, as this was the only time I could have a bar of chocolate for breakfast without being nagged—in fact, we pretty much spent the whole morning eating chocolate.

One of the loudest toys that year was the bagatelle, a pinball-like game, which was about 12 inches high. It had apparently survived being dropped down the stairs the night before when the sacks were being carried up to our beds. I also got a deluxe Magic set so that I could learn some tricks. Also, thankfully, the girliest thing I got that year were *Bunty* and *Judy* annuals. This was such an improvement over the dolls from the year before (most of which were still gathering dust somewhere in the house).

Father Christmas also had the foresight to buy me a cowgirl's costume. This consisted of a cowgirl hat, fringed bolero with sheriff's star on it, and a fringed skirt. I was so proud to see that I even had a toy gun with a holster to wear. At long last, I had been given something that a boy would be given, a gun, just like my younger brother had. I smiled all day long and was hard pressed to change into my brown party suit later on in the day. This was so far the best Christmas ever; Mum had already outdone herself.

Christmas dinner always consisted of the massive Christmas turkey with potatoes roasted in lard (animal fat), Brussels sprouts, peas, roasted parsnips and sage, and onion stuffing with little chipolata sausages. All served with Bisto gravy and mint sauce, in our house we always had mint sauce with every roast meal, not just roast lamb. This feast was followed by Christmas pudding for the adults and for us children, ice cream.

The cooking of the turkey invariably overloaded the electrical circuits and Dad had to fetch the ladder to reach the fuse box, which was beside the front door and 10 feet up the wall, near the ceiling. Dad was ably assisted by Uncle, who was pressed into service as ladder holder for this event. The large white blown fuse was duly replaced with a new one and the cooking of the turkey continued unabated. It happened so frequently that it almost became a part of the Christmas Day activities.

A few hours later, we all sat down to dinner, with the now fully cooked turkey in pride of place on the table. Now no Christmas dinner was complete without crackers. A Christmas cracker had to be pulled part way through the meal so that for the rest of the dinner you would have a crown-shaped paper hat on your head and could read each other silly jokes from the crackers. No one was exempt from wearing the paper crowns; both young and old were obliged to put them on.

After dinner, while the women washed dishes and tidied up (a task that thankfully I was considered too young to be included in), my brother and I would get back to the serious stuff of playing with our new toys.

By 3 o'clock, we (me still resplendent in my cowgirl outfit) all gathered around the radio waiting for Her Majesty to begin her Christmas message. The Queen's speech was usually on TV but because the Queen was pregnant and could not be seen in public, we only heard her voice and the message was only a few minutes long. After the speech, we watched the family movie accompanied by the gentle sound of Dad and Uncle snoring in the only two armchairs.

Tea was always cold turkey sandwiches with Branston pickle and mince pies. Mum told my brother and me to put on our party clothes, and so I reluctantly took off my cowgirl outfit and put on my smart brown 'Chanel' suit.

I was in the living room watching Dad and Uncle put the chairs against the wall for the Christmas guests to sit on when the doorbell rang. It was still too early for party guests and everyone was busy so I shouted that I would get it. I ran downstairs in my grown-up outfit.

I opened the door to find…Anthony standing there! I just stared at him, the love of my now 11-year-old life, and here he was back again right in front of me. Mum shouted, 'Who is it?' and I called back that it was Anthony. She said nothing, no comments, no instructions; she just kept quiet. He reached out and touched my hand and I got that warm feeling of being with my friend again, the one person who knew me so well and who I could always trust. Then he leaned forward and kissed me on the lips. I just stared into his eyes, knowing that I could stand there forever looking at his face.

I waited for the rattling of the windows from Mum but there was nothing—just me and Anthony. I had almost lost him, and I never wanted to lose him again because this kiss made everything different. I wanted more of this kiss, this grown-up stuff. I wanted more than just the hand-holding feeling; it was something special just between the two of us. (And for once I did not even *think* of asking about Cyril.)

Anthony said he had missed my smile and the folded paper messages with the little 'x's' in them. He told me that Cyril, his hamster, was doing well in his new home. Then he asked how I was—I think I managed to say that I was okay—and then he said he had to get back to his uncle's house on the next road. He let go of my hand and gave me a piece of paper with his new address written on it.

I gripped the address tightly and watched him leave like it was a dream, or maybe the best Christmas present ever! I stood there for I don't know how long and then eventually closed the door and almost floated back up the stairs to the living room.

By the time I got to the top of the stairs my head was

beginning to clear and I was jolted back to reality by the sound of Mum's voice giving instructions about chair placements. I took a deep breath and became Jill, the daughter, again but before rejoining everyone, I ran up to my bedroom and put the precious address in my jewellery box to keep it, and my heart, safe.

Back in the living room, every available chair in the house had now been arranged against the living room walls for our guests: The room was now ready for our party. In one corner was the Beautility teak table, which had been pressed into service as the bar top but, of course, suitably covered with its protective rubber matting. The bottles of illicit whiskey and gin were proudly on show on top of the 'bar'. The brown ale, beer, and lemonade were still in their wooden crates and stacked on the floor. There were what seemed to be dozens and dozens of glasses—beer glasses, short glasses for whiskey, and long glasses for gin. The bright orange ice bucket with the gold-coloured knob was awaiting some ice cubes from the tiny freezer in our fridge. It seemed like a lot of to-do for the small party we were about to have.

At around 7 o'clock, people began to arrive, all dressed up in their best Christmas clothes, or as Mum would say 'dressed to the nines'. The women all wore dresses with stiletto heels and all the men wore shirts with ties, some with cardigans and a few with suits, and all had newly polished shoes. The women's hair was backcombed into a bouffant style and the men's hair was slicked down and short above the collar.

As I played the role of door opener, with everyone else busy, I would be the first to witness the shortage of guests. My happiness over Anthony was evaporating and I had a growing empty feeling that I couldn't quite explain. My whole world was the people around me, my relatives and friends, and they were all disappearing. There were spaces that the people in my life used to fill and all that was left behind now was a numbing emptiness. It felt as if I was just standing looking at the picture of my life, and where those people used to be, there were now just blank black holes. I didn't understand it but I did know that it felt horrible. I just sat there on the bottom step of the stairs in the hallway, all by myself, hoping that the doorbell would ring.

It didn't ring for ages. Then suddenly it rang twice and I opened the door to find Uncle John and Uncle Earn, their wives, and my cousins. Well, I thought that was probably it for the night. Pretty much everyone else had moved to Bracknell: this strange city had all my relatives in it; it was miles away and I would never see them again.

But then…slowly but surely, more and more relatives and friends appeared at the door. Some had told Mum of their plans but others decided to just show up and make a surprise of it. The party grew to a number that was probably a hundred but seemed like a thousand to me. It was as though everyone in the world had come to our party! At least for now life felt a little bit normal. I somehow suspected that it wasn't going to last but at least on Christmas Day it felt like the world I used to know and that made me feel good. I could hear the adults talking upstairs and the music begin to play. Mum shouted downstairs that I could stop being a door opener and join everyone else.

In pride of place at our parties was the radiogram, the media centre of the day. A radiogram was a piece of furniture about 4 feet long and 3 feet high. Inside were speakers for the radio and a turntable for playing records, with a large area for the 78 and 33 rpm records to be stored in. There was no virtual 'cloud' storage in those days.

The records we had were by Elvis, Fats Domino, Doris Day, and Max Bygraves. The Beatles were all over the charts but Mum and Dad did not approve of these long-haired singers who they looked down upon as being untidy and well, 'It isn't really music, is it!' So Elvis, Matt Monro, and Max Bygraves was as modern as we got. We also had the old favourite cockney songs, such as *I've Got a Lovely Bunch of Coconuts* and *Knees up Mother Brown*. It was the old cockney songs that got everyone up and dancing. There was always lots of dancing; in fact, when it came to *Knees up Mother Brown* and you had about 50 people dancing, the wooden floor would flex a bit and the needle would skip on the record because of the vibrations. A couple of men were always given the task of holding down the radiogram to stop it from bouncing on the floor. The music was turned up really loud but Mum had the foresight to invite all the neighbours to come along to avoid any complaints.

Looking at the laughing faces and people jumping up and

down to the rhythm of the music, it was hard to think that this might be the last Christmas with us all together. They had made the special trip this year but what about next year? It seemed to me that my whole world was leaving Lamlash. These happy, smiling people had all lived through the most horrific of times. They had sent their sons off to war and left their wives, children, and parents at home; they had lived through having bombs falling on them every night. At last it was a time of peace, now that the war was over, and they hoped that they would now get that better tomorrow that they had fought for.

At the party as usual, later in the evening, Nan's friend, Arthur, played the spoons. He used two back to back spoons clutched in one hand to play a song by banging them on his arms, hands, and legs. We all sat around and watched as Arthur performed his usual party piece. It was then our turn and my brother and I sang our usual duet of *Silent Night*, which was Nan's favourite Christmas carol. All this entertainment was recorded on a reel-to-reel tape player—we had all the latest gadgets—and we played it back a few days later.

Everyone had shown up for the party this year, all our friends as well as our relatives. It was a great send-off. Ruth and Lewis, farm people that I stayed with the previous summer, had driven up for Christmas all the way from Kineton in Warwickshire. This was quite a feat as they drove the 140 miles in their three-wheeler bubble car. Those tiny little cars with a glass bubble roof had a top speed of 53 mph, depending upon wind conditions, as the car had trouble remaining upright if it was too windy. It would take Ruth and Lewis six hours to get from Kineton to London, with a few stops along the way. These two-seater vehicles, without a boot for luggage storage, were cramped and constantly smelled of leaking petrol.

Johnny Rocco, who had helped Dad become a cabbie, was there with his family. Pat and his wife, who were long-time friends of Mum and Dad, were also there. And, of course, all the uncles, aunts, and cousins from the Clarks and the Walters families showed up.

Even Rex, the dog, made a brief appearance! Rex had been banished to the kitchen but managed to escape when Auntie went to fetch a cloth to mop up a spill. Rex sneaked his head around the door, saw all the fun, and in no time was wagging his tail and jumping up and down along with the dancing relatives. That is until he was spotted by Mum, who then escorted him back to the kitchen. Rex had a long and happy life with us. Mum would make home-cooked food for him and I would cut up animal hearts for him to eat. When we later moved into a house with a garden, he would enjoy the grass and the dirt immensely. Occasionally, Rex would escape and my brother and I would run over to the field next door to retrieve him. As he got older, he had a special chair to sleep on with a bright red shiny cover with a gold filigree pattern. He lived to a ripe old age and was well loved. He is still missed—just a little.

As the party wound down, sandwiches were served and cups of tea offered at 10 o'clock to help sober people up. By 11 o'clock, people started to drift way, tired but merry from the drink. They said their goodbyes as if nothing had changed but we all knew that it had. We were all going off into the great unknown and without the support of family and friends. The war must have been terrifying enough but this seemed worse because we were losing one another.

A week later, on Old Year's Night, Mum went to the back door to let the old year out and then to the front door to let the New Year in. This year we had no idea what we were letting in the front door; hopefully, it would be good and worth all the sacrifices that everyone had made for a better future.

EPILOGUE

After the party that Christmas, we saw some family members a couple of times but it was never the same again. The constant stream of aunts and uncles (with cousins in tow) dropping round for a chat about the latest crisis had stopped. The family had left for a better life, with a better future for their children, but in doing so they had given up our close-knit way of living and said goodbye to their own cockney roots.

Auntie and Uncle were two of the last to leave; it felt as if one day they were just not there and I was left all alone. They, my cousins, and my Anthony were all gone (although Anthony and I did at least write). The house was empty, the street was empty, school was empty.

A week after Auntie and Uncle moved out, an old lady (a stranger to us) moved into their suite. Mum didn't like the idea that this woman could just walk upstairs into our part of Lamlash. The house didn't feel safe anymore and neither did the community.

So Mum decided that we, too, would move to a place outside London called Bexleyheath in the county of Kent.

This time, though, we would not rent a house; we would buy. The rest of the family thought that Mum was mad to have the millstone of a mortgage around her neck but Mum was determined. We barely had the money for the move but somehow it happened. It was the hardest thing ever to leave 11b Lamlash Street, but as a child, we just did what we were told. Life in Kent was so very different from London but that is another story.

Lamlash Street has long since been demolished. It lay bare for many years, just an empty, neglected space in the middle of London. Then following the 2012 London Olympics, there was a community initiative to convert the space into a garden area. And so there arose Lamlash Gardens. More recently, there was another project to rejuvenate Fives Court, that shortcut to school of mine of Jack the Ripper potential.

The new community may be different from the cockney Londoner people that I knew but nonetheless, Lamlash Street (Lamlash Gardens) continues to be at its heart, and the community is as loyal and steadfast as the one that I knew.

As I sit here 50 years later, with my graduate degree and a 30-year work history as a professional, I have a lot to thank those Victorian philanthropists for. I was taken from the working classes—the lowest class, really—and thanks to a good education, a determined mother, and good housing, I was able to change my future for the better. Our family transformed itself from starving poor to middle-class affluence—and wondering how much to leave the children in our wills.

Printed in Great Britain
by Amazon

71249192R00092